Practical English Workbook

Practical English Workbook

Third Edition

Floyd C. Watkins
Emory University

William B. Dillingham
Emory University

John T. Hiers
Valdosta State College

Houghton Mifflin Company   Boston
Dallas   Geneva, Ill.   Lawrenceville, N.J.   Palo Alto

Grateful acknowledgment is made to the following publishers and authors for permission to reprint from their works:

The American Heritage Dictionary, Second College Edition. Definition of *bureaucrat.* © 1985 by Houghton Mifflin Company. Reprinted by permission from *The American Heritage Dictionary, Second College Edition.*

William A. Henry, "Journalism Under Fire." Copyright 1983 Time Inc. All rights reserved. Reprinted by permission from *Time.*

Norman Myers, "By Saving Wild Species, We May Be Saving Ourselves." Originally published in the Nov./Dec. 1983 *TNC News.* Reprinted by permission of *The Nature Conservancy News.*

Francis Parkman, *The Oregon Trail.* Riverside Literature Series, edited with introduction and notes. Copyright © 1925 by Houghton Mifflin Company. Adapted by permission.

John Rockwell, "Blues, and Other Noises, in the Night." © 1976 *Saturday Review* magazine. Reprinted by permission.

ISBN: 0-395-36401-9

ABCDEFGHIJ-A-93210/898765

Contents

17 Connotation, Figurative Language, and Vocabulary 277

18 Paragraph Unity 291

Preface

The organization of the Third Edition of the *Practical English Workbook* closely follows that of the *Practical English Handbook*, Seventh Edition. For those students who require more practice with basic skills, this workbook is designed to reinforce the instruction of the handbook with parallel lessons, additional examples, and varied exercises. Beginning with parts of speech, the workbook also provides lessons on parts of sentences, sentence errors, punctuation, mechanics, diction and style, and paragraph unity. The logical sequence of these lessons makes the *Practical English Workbook* adaptable to other texts as well as to independent study and laboratory instruction for students at all levels.

As with the Second Edition, we have attempted to make the style of the Third Edition concise and readable, avoiding the extremes of colloquialism and rigid formality. This edition, as did its predecessor, stresses clarity and precision. We have updated and expanded instruction in the Third Edition. We have added more illustrations and more explanations of why an example is correct, and we have revised extensively many of the exercises. We have expanded the sections on the paragraph and the dictionary.

Like the *Practical English Handbook*, this edition of the *Practical English Workbook* follows a traditional approach to grammar, punctuation, and syntax. We believe that this method has proven itself over the years as the best means to call attention to writing problems and to improve the writing skills of students. This mainstream approach to grammar, punctuation, and syntax has dictated the workbook's methodology. We have worked toward stating the most useful rules in the simplest form possible and have stressed typical problems in both examples and exercises. Throughout the text, emphasis is upon building writing skills and developing the student's understanding of the well-established practices governing the use of the English language.

We are deeply indebted to Professor James O. Williams of Valdosta State College for his aid and advice. We also wish to thank Joyce Benson, State University of New York; Barbara Carson, University of Georgia; Basil Clark, Saginaw Valley State College; Vivian I. Davis, Tarrant Junior College South; C. Jeriel Howard, Northeastern Illinois University; and T. Mark Ledbetter, Emory University, for their thoughtful reading of the manuscript.

F. C. W.
W. B. D.
J. T. H.

Grammar

1

The Parts of Speech

There are eight parts of speech in the English language: nouns, pronouns, verbs, adjectives, adverbs, conjunctions, prepositions, and interjections.

NOUNS

Nouns are words that name. There are five kinds of nouns: proper nouns, common nouns, collective nouns, abstract nouns, and concrete nouns.

(a) **Proper nouns** name particular persons, places, or things (*Thomas Edison, Chicago, Kleenex*).

Commodore Perry sailed to *Japan* on the U.S.S. *Mississippi.*

(b) **Common nouns** name one or more of a class or group (*doctor, pilots, artists*).

The *voters* were not deterred by *snow.*

(c) **Collective nouns** name a whole group, though they are singular in form (*senate, jury, clergy*).

The *audience* applauds loudly.

(d) **Abstract nouns** name concepts, beliefs, or qualities (*truth, energy, humor*).

Freedom implies *responsibility.*

(e) **Concrete nouns** name things experienced through the senses (*fire, coffee, roses*).

I prepared a small *plate* of *crackers* and *cheese.*

PRONOUNS

There are seven kinds of pronouns. Most pronouns are used in place of nouns, although indefinite pronouns do not refer to any particular noun.

2

(a) **Demonstrative pronouns** summarize in one word the content of a statement that has already been made. They may be singular *(this, that)* or plural *(these, those)*.

Fruit, bran, whole wheat—*these* are common sources of healthful fiber.

(b) **Indefinite pronouns** do not indicate a particular person or thing. They are usually singular. The most common indefinite pronouns are *any, anybody, anyone, everybody, everyone, neither, none, one,* and *some*.

Anybody may apply for a scholarship.

(c) **Intensive pronouns** end in *-self* or *-selves (herself, themselves)*. An intensive pronoun emphasizes a word that precedes it in the sentence.

She *herself* was surprised at her quick success.

The committee *itself* was confused.

(d) **Interrogative pronouns** *(what, which, who, whom, whose, whoever, whomever)* are used in questions.

Which is mine?

What are we going to do tonight?

(e) **Personal pronouns** usually refer to a person or a group of people, but may refer to an object or objects. They have many forms depending on their grammatical function.

We need *her* on the team to help *us* play better.

Put *it* on the table.

	SINGULAR	PLURAL
First person	I, me, mine	we, us, ours
Second person	you, yours	you, yours
Third person	he, she, it, him, her, his, hers, its	they, them, theirs

(f) **Reflexive pronouns** end in *-self* or *-selves* and indicate that the action of the verb returns to the subject.

He caught *himself* making the same mistake twice.

The broken flywheel caused the machine to destroy *itself*.

(g) **Relative pronouns** *(who, whom, whoever, whomever, whichever, whose, that, what, which)* are used to introduce dependent adjective and noun clauses.

You can eat the pie *that is in the refrigerator.* (adjective clause modifying *pie*, introduced by the relative pronoun *that*)

The workers *who had finished* began to leave. (noun clause)

VERBS

Verbs assert an action or express a condition.

The bus *screeched* to a stop. (verb showing *action*)

The capital of Missouri *is* Jefferson City. (verb showing *condition*)

Verbs that show *condition* are called **linking verbs.** The most common linking verbs are forms of the verb *to be (is, are, was, were).* Other linking verbs are *seem, become, look, appear, feel, sound, smell,* and *taste.*

The passengers *were* sleepy. (linking verb showing condition of sleep)

Main verbs may have **auxiliary verbs,** or helpers, such as *are, have, may, will.*

The school band *has* left the field.

ADJECTIVES

Adjectives are descriptive words that modify nouns or pronouns. The **definite article** *the* and the **indefinite articles** *a* and *an* are also classified as adjectives.

The howling dog kept us awake.

Predicate adjectives follow linking verbs and modify the subject of the sentence.

This milk is *fresh.*

The car looks *new.*

Some **possessive adjectives** have forms that are similar to possessive pronouns: *my, your, her, his, its, their.* These adjectives refer to specific nouns just as pronouns do but function as adjectives. *Your, our,* and *their* end with *s* in the pronoun form.

Your dinner is ready.

Demonstrative adjectives and demonstrative pronouns have the same forms: *this, that, these, those.* (See demonstrative pronouns, p. 2.)

This comment is helpful. (*This* modifies *comment.*)

This is a helpful comment. (*This* is used here as a demonstrative pronoun.)

Indefinite adjectives resemble indefinite pronouns: *some, many, most, every*.

Every employee received a bonus. (*Every* modifies *employee*.)
Everyone left. (*Everyone* is an indefinite pronoun.)

ADVERBS

Adverbs describe, qualify, or limit verbs (and verbals), adjectives, and other adverbs.

She left *quickly*. (adverb—modifies a verb)
Talking *fast*, she soon was out of breath. (adverb—modifies the verbal *talking*)
The train was *very* late. (adverb—modifies the adjective *late*)
We'll be through *very* soon. (adverb—modifies another adverb *soon*)

Many adverbs are formed by adding *-ly* to adjectives; others express place or time: *soon, later, always, forever, there, out*.

Bring the newspaper *inside*. (*Inside* expresses *place*.)
Bring me the newspaper *now*. (*Now* expresses *time*.)

CONJUNCTIONS

Conjunctions connect words, phrases, and clauses. Conjunctive adverbs—*therefore, however, furthermore, moreover*—connect clauses and phrases.

Conversion vans use much gas; *nevertheless*, they remain popular for long trips.

Coordinating conjunctions—*and, but, or, nor, for, yet, so*—connect sentence elements that are of equal rank.

John *and* Mary are visiting us today. (conjunction joining two nouns)
We needed to talk to you, *but* your telephone was always busy. (conjunction joining two independent clauses)

Subordinating conjunctions introduce a dependent element in a sentence—that is, one that cannot stand alone as a sentence. Some common subordinating conjunctions are *although, because, if, since, unless*, and *when*.

When we finished the test. (dependent element, not a sentence)
When we finished the test, we turned in our papers. (dependent element joined to independent clause to form a complete sentence)
We were tired *because we had studied all night*. (dependent element joined to independent clause to form a complete sentence)

PREPOSITIONS

Prepositions are connective words that join nouns or pronouns to other words in a sentence to form a unit (called a **prepositional phrase**). Prepositional phrases usually function as either adjectives or adverbs. Some prepositions are *above, at, before, by, from, in, into, of, over, through, up,* and *with.* Some groups of words (*according to, in spite of, along with*) may also function as prepositions.

The jet flew *through the clouds.* (*Through the clouds* is a prepositional phrase used as an adverb to modify the verb *flew.*)

The woman *in the car* is my mother (*In the car* is a prepositional phrase used as an adjective to modify the noun *woman.*)

Some words that resemble prepositions function as adverbs:

Go out. (*out* used as adverb)

Go out the door. (*out* used as preposition)

Some words such as *before* and *after* may function as prepositions or subordinating conjunctions.

INTERJECTIONS

Interjections are words that express surprise or strong emotions. They may stand alone or be part of a sentence. Interjections usually are avoided in formal writing.

Wow!

Well, you should have been more careful.

1.1 Nouns

■ *Underline the words used as nouns in the following sentences.*

EXAMPLES

Educational <u>television</u> needs private <u>donations</u>.

Good relief <u>pitching</u> is essential for successful baseball <u>teams</u>.

<u>Ronald Reagan</u> succeeded <u>Jimmy Carter</u> as President.

1. Community historical societies plan the restoration of old buildings.

2. Several archaeological excavations clarify the Biblical accounts of the era of Solomon.

3. Road atlases provide convenient guides for cross-country travelers.

4. Whole-grain cereals yield much valuable protein.

5. Early in the century 200 button-making factories in the United States almost depleted the supply of fresh-water mussels.

6. Some veterinarians have found acupuncture to be of value in the treatment of animals.

7. The Galapagos Islands, volcanic in origin and isolated in the Pacific Ocean, offer many biological wonders.

8. Selenium in small doses is a necessary part of the human diet.

9. State laws require annual vaccination against rabies for all dogs and cats.

10. Genetic engineering will revolutionize agriculture, mining, and medicine.

1.2 Pronouns

■ *Underline the pronouns in the following sentences.*

EXAMPLES

<u>She</u> <u>herself</u> intends to represent the clients. (personal, intensive pronouns)

Reserved tickets are available for <u>those</u> <u>who</u> wait at gate G, <u>which</u> is on the north side of the stadium. (demonstrative, relative, relative pronouns)

<u>What</u> should <u>everyone</u> try for dessert? (interrogative, indefinite pronouns)

1. Nobody spoke against the proposal, but each of us had reasons to object to it.

2. Some of the criticism in his latest review is especially harsh.

3. You will almost always find Edie playing a video game because she enjoys the challenge.

4. All of the silver needs polishing before we set the table.

5. Fortunately, none of the crop was ruined by the ice storm.

6. Those locked in the glass case are the most valuable items in the store.

7. Harry and his wife promised themselves that they would do their holiday shopping earlier next year.

8. Whoever succeeds, even by honest means, will find he has his critics.

9. The problem itself was easy to understand, but the solution required working through several steps.

10. Whatever they did to follow their budget, they rarely managed to stay within it.

1.3 Verbs

■ *Underline the verbs in the following sentences.*

EXAMPLES

Technology <u>raises</u> hope for greater crop yields. (action verb)

Most snakes <u>are</u> harmless. (linking verb showing condition)

Economists <u>will remain</u> optimistic about the recovery. (auxiliary verb and linking verb showing condition)

1. Attics often are cleaned and then converted into additional bedrooms.

2. Many athletes fail, not because they are out of condition but because they develop mental blocks.

3. The movie was so popular that it was held over for another week.

4. The children went to the doctor and had their annual physical examinations.

5. A congressional committee on housing will be in the Midwest to discuss the special needs of local communities.

6. People once believed that toothaches were a sign that some god was angered.

7. Before a mechanic gives his estimate for repairs, he usually suggests that the customer sit down.

8. The lighting in the restaurant was so low that the diners could hardly read the menu.

9. The conveniences that most enjoy in their lives today would have required the labor of at least eighty servants a century ago.

10. Did the electrician follow your directions, or did he find the house by himself?

1.4 Adjectives

■ *Underline the words used as adjectives in the following sentences. Remember that articles (a, an, the) are also classified as adjectives.*

EXAMPLES

<u>Hot</u>, <u>dry</u> days and <u>cool</u>, <u>windy</u> nights characterize <u>most</u> deserts.

<u>The</u> herd became <u>anxious</u> when <u>the</u> <u>bad</u> storm hit. (predicate adjective following the linking verb *became*)

1. The puzzled historian stared at the faded painting of the royal couple.

2. At the circus the children laughed and clapped as fifteen clowns emerged from the small car.

3. In 1904 the famous Geronimo rode in the inaugural parade of Theodore Roosevelt.

4. Some winter campers use small propane heaters to combat cold weather.

5. Tremendous ovations that follow performances please young performers.

6. Oceanographic teams study the fragile sea life along the coral reefs near Key West, Florida.

7. We left the porch light on because our expected guest had not arrived.

8. The late movie was a film made in the 1930s.

9. Barnacles covered the rusty hull of the old ship that had run aground last week during the destructive typhoon.

10. A leaky garbage disposal usually causes water to stream across a kitchen floor.

1.5 Adverbs

■ *Underline the words used as adverbs in the following sentences.*

EXAMPLES

<u>More</u> modest increases in prices <u>usually</u> are expected. (adverb modifying an adjective and a verb)

The game ended <u>very</u> <u>quickly</u>. (adverb modifying another adverb and adverb modifying a verb)

1. The city council meets weekly now.

2. The office seldom closes before five o'clock.

3. Caterpillars move slowly but purposefully up the stems of plants.

4. Our new merchandise will arrive soon.

5. Because surgeons work cautiously with lasers, some procedures take longer than usual.

6. The railroad tracks ran westward and disappeared at the edge of the mountains.

7. While carefully examining the walls of the ancient building, the archaeologist suddenly discovered a small cache of coins that easily were over 2,000 years old.

8. The flowers were covered partially by late spring frost that quickly melted when the sun rose.

9. As the morning fog quietly rolled in over the city, the traffic gradually slowed.

10. Candidates who speak forcefully rather than deliberately often are more effective with voters.

1.6 Conjunctions, Prepositions, and Interjections

■ *Underline prepositions in the following sentences once, conjunctions twice, and interjections three times.*

EXAMPLES

Ugh, this glass of milk is too warm, and I need another one. (interjection, preposition, coordinating conjunction)

Although the winds were strong, the boaters began the race for the gold cup. (subordinating conjunction, preposition)

1. The actress looked at the script and pointed out several weak scenes.

2. Throughout the afternoon, the school held a series of seminars on financial planning.

3. Birds build nests in chimneys, and these must be removed before winter.

4. Often researchers find themselves on the brink of discoveries far more important than they originally imagined.

5. Experimental results should be checked carefully, for later findings may depend on them.

6. "Well, if this letter doesn't work," the disgruntled consumer said, "I'll write again."

7. The jury admired the defense attorney's animated closing argument, but it did not acquit his client.

8. "No!" responded the officer. "I do not accept your answer."

9. The rain came early in the morning, so the yard work was postponed.

10. People do not seem to realize the need to conserve energy, nor do they comprehend the consequences if they do not.

1.7 Same Word; Several Functions

■ *Many words can function as several parts of speech. Compose very brief sentences with the following words, illustrating the parts of speech in parentheses. If necessary, check a dictionary.*

EXAMPLES

right (noun) *The jury had to decide what was right in the complex case.*

right (adjective) *The right side of the highway was beautiful in its spring colors.*

right (adverb) *The new attorney rose right to the top of his profession.*

1. like (preposition) _____

_____

_____

(adjective) _____

_____

_____

(verb) _____

_____

_____

2. water (noun) _____

_____

_____

(verb) _____

_____

_____

(adjective) _____

_____

_____

3. well (noun) _____

_____

_____

(interjection) _____

_____

_____

(adverb) _____

_____

_____

4. light (noun) _____

_____

_____

(adjective) _____

_____

_____

(verb) _____

_____

_____

5. open (adjective) _____

_____

_____

(noun) _____

_____

_____

(verb) _____

_____

_____

6. house (noun) _____

_____

_____

(adjective) _____

_____

_____

(verb) _____

_____

_____

7. total (noun) _____

_____

_____

(adjective) _____

_____

_____

(verb) _____

_____

_____

8. paint (noun) _____

_____

_____

(adjective) _____

_____

_____

(verb) _____

_____

_____

9. paper (noun) _____

_____

_____

(verb) _____

_____

_____

(adjective) _____

_____

_____

10. down (noun) _____

_____

_____

(verb) _____

_____

_____

(preposition) _____

_____

_____

2

The Parts of Sentences

SUBJECTS AND PREDICATES

A sentence has a complete meaning and can stand on its own. Its essential parts are its subject and predicate.

The **subject** does something, has something done to it, or is described.

The *woman* is reading. (subject acting)

Books are read. (subject acted upon)

Books are interesting. (subject described)

In sentences that command, a subject may be understood.

Go to the den. (*you* is the understood subject)

The **predicate** says something about the subject.

The woman *is reading*.

Books *are sources of information*.

Books *are interesting*.

The **simple subject** usually consists of one word. The **complete subject** consists of all the words that function together as the subject.

The *house* is dark. (simple subject)

The old house is dark. (complete subject)

When similar units of a sentence are linked together and function together, they are termed **compound**.

The automobile and *the truck* stopped. (compound subject)

The verb in a sentence is called the **simple predicate**. The simple predicate, its modifiers, and any complements are called the **complete predicate**.

Harry *finished* his work. (simple predicate)

Harry *finished his work*. (complete predicate)

She *researched* the topic and *wrote* the paper. (compound predicate)

COMPLEMENTS

Complements complete the meaning of the sentence. They are predicate adjectives, predicate nominatives, direct objects, and indirect objects. Predicate adjectives and predicate nominatives are also called **subjective complements.**

Predicate adjectives follow linking verbs and describe the subject.

Our neighbor is *tall*. (predicate adjective describing *neighbor*)

The fresh tomato tastes *sweet*. (predicate adjective after linking verb)

Predicate nominatives are nouns that follow linking verbs and rename the subject.

Our neighbor is an *actor*. (predicate nominative renaming neighbor)

Direct objects receive the action of a transitive verb.

We played *Scrabble*. (direct object telling what was played)

Indirect objects receive the action of the verb indirectly. When the preposition *to* or *for* is understood, the word is an indirect object. A sentence with an indirect object must also have a direct object.

Sheila gave *me* a present. (indirect object telling *to whom* the present was given)

Objective complements accompany direct objects. They may modify the object or be synonymous with it.

The new owner painted his house *red*. (adjective modifying the direct object *house*)

PHRASES

A **phrase** is a group of words that does not have both a subject and a predicate.

A **noun phrase** consists of a noun and its modifiers.

The new computer programmer started yesterday.

An **appositive phrase** renames a noun.

The Pentagon, *the largest office building in the world*, is located in Washington, D.C.

A **verb phrase** consists of the main verb and its helping verbs.

The house *is being painted*.

Prepositional phrases function as adjectives or adverbs.

The door *to the closet* is open. (adjectival phrase modifying *door*)

The rain fell *in the park*. (adverbial phrase modifying *fell*)

VERBALS AND VERBAL PHRASES

A **verbal** is formed from a verb. Three kinds of verbals are gerunds, participles, and infinitives.

Gerunds

A **gerund** always ends in *-ing* and functions as a noun.

Swimming is fun. (gerund as subject)

Swimming in the high surf after the storm is exciting. (gerund phrase as subject)

Participles

Participles usually end in *-ing, -ed, -d, -t,* or *-n*. They function as adjectives.

Tired of reading, he decided to take a short walk. (modifies *he; tired of reading* is the complete participial phrase)

Encouraging to the board of directors, the report predicted record profits. (modifies *report; encouraging to the board of directors* is the complete participial phrase)

Infinitives

Infinitives usually begin with *to*, which is followed by a verb. They function as nouns, adjectives, or adverbs.

To show the new student around our school took time. (infinitive phrase as subject)

Camera cases *to be carried on the trip* must be waterproof. (infinitive phrase as adjective)

To be certain of lodging, one should make reservations. (infinitive phrase as adverb)

The children helped their father *plant the garden*. (infinitive phrase without *to*)

CLAUSES

Clauses are groups of words with subjects and predicates. Clauses are either independent or dependent (sometimes called *subordinate).*

An **independent clause** can stand alone as a complete sentence. Two or more independent clauses may be linked (1) by coordinating conjunctions *(and, but, or, nor, for, so, yet)* and a comma, (2) by a semicolon, or (3) by a semicolon and a **conjunctive adverb** (such as *however, therefore, moreover, nevertheless, otherwise*).

The circus is over, *and* the workers are cleaning the grounds. (two independent clauses connected by a comma and a coordinating conjunction)

The river was crowded with barges; each one of them was piled high with coal from the mines of Kentucky and West Virginia. (two independent clauses joined by a semicolon)

Low clouds obscured much of the mountain; *however,* the snow-covered peak sparkled in the bright sunlight. (two independent clauses joined by a semicolon and a conjunctive adverb)

A **dependent** or **subordinate clause** may function as a noun, an adjective, or an adverb.

Who the guest speaker was to be is a mystery. (noun clause as subject)

Anyone *who helps* will be paid. (adjective clause modifying *anyone*)

When the game started, we stood up. (adverb clause modifying *stood*)

2.1 The Parts of Sentences

■ *Underline the simple or compound subjects once and the simple or compound predicates twice. Identify complements with the abbreviations **p.a.** (predicate adjective), **p.n.** (predicate nominative), **d.o.** (direct object), **i.o.** (indirect object), and **o.c.** (objective complement) above the appropriate words.*

EXAMPLES

Tourists <u>took</u> many photographs of the new office complexes. *d.o.*

Geologists <u>gave</u> investors the preliminary analysis of several oil wells. *i.o.* *d.o.*

1. The solution to the dilemma came only after long study.

2. Water from the lake cascaded through the open spillway.

3. Contrast and repetition are the two main ingredients in musical form.

4. Clouds are minute particles of water or ice.

5. Brahms wrote four symphonies.

6. Interesting floral arrangements contain a profusion of blossoms.

7. Spanish treasure ships laden with gold, silver, and gems are still being discovered in the Caribbean.

8. At airshows stunt pilots put their planes into steep power stalls and then slip into dives.

9. The headlines reported the arrival of the delegates to the economic conference.

10. The blackberry is edible, and it is used often in pastries.

2.2 The Parts of Sentences

■ *Underline the simple or compound subjects once and the simple or compound predicates twice. Identify complements with the abbreviations p.a. (predicate adjective), p.n. (predicate nominative), d.o. (direct object), and i.o. (indirect object) above the appropriate words.*

EXAMPLES
$\qquad\qquad\qquad\qquad\qquad\qquad$ *p.a.*
The <u>researchers</u> and <u>photographers</u> <u><u>were</u></u> hungry after the field trip.

$\qquad$ *p.n.*
<u>She</u> <u><u>became</u></u> president of the holding company last week.

1. At family reunions, grandparents often regale their grandchildren with outrageous stories about their youth.

2. Plans for the 1988 Olympics are almost completed.

3. A master forger can paint almost perfect copies of famous works of art.

4. Hungarian composer Franz Liszt was instrumental in shaping the career of Johannes Brahms.

5. Latin America was settled primarily by Europeans from Spain and Portugal.

6. Arthur Wynne devised the first crossword puzzle in 1913 for the *New York World*.

7. The International Balloon Fiesta takes place each year in Albuquerque, New Mexico.

8. A common use of computers is for games.

9. Salaries for federal employees are highest in Alaska.

10. One notices immediately the differences between the two cultures, especially in their art.

2.3 Phrases

■ *On the blank lines, indicate whether the italicized phrase is used as subject, modifier, or verb, and indicate its function in the sentence.*

EXAMPLES

Using credit cards is a way *of life* for modern Americans.

modifier - prepositional phrase modifying noun way

The scientists, *concerned about the potential hazards,* wanted the latest research findings made public.

modifier - participial phrase modifying noun scientists

Keeping their bodies in good condition is a primary concern of many young Americans.

subject - gerund phrase as subject of is

1. The error *in his bank statement* was traced to a computer.

_____

2. The children raced to the corner *to catch their bus.*

_____

3. *Talking with an insurance agent* makes people realize that they need additional coverage for their home.

_____

4. *To date fossil remains* requires several hours of careful laboratory work.

_____

5. The boy's sole ambition was to *score six million on his new video game.*

_____

6. The chinook winds whip down the eastern slopes of the Rocky Mountains and sweep *across the vast prairies.*

_____

7. Construction *of the new civic center and parkway* revived the sagging economy of downtown businesses.

   _____

8. On each side of the highway were hundreds of billboards *advertising everything* from modern motels to roadside stands that sell fresh fruit and bedspreads.

   _____

9. Many auto mechanics *have returned* to school to study electronics; thus they will be able to repair the electronic parts being built into new automobiles.

   _____

10. *The tour bus* stopped in Savannah so that the tourists could visit the beautiful old homes and the sections of town that date back to the last part of the eighteenth century.

   _____

2.4 Phrases

■ *Write sentences containing the following words in the prescribed phrases.*

EXAMPLE
preparing; verb phrase as simple predicate of subject *we*

This afternoon we shall be preparing diskettes for word processing.

1. *concerned;* participial phrase modifying a subject and placed before the verb

   _____

   _____

   _____

2. *to hear;* infinitive phrase used as an object

   _____

   _____

   _____

3. *giving;* gerund phrase used as an object of a preposition

   _____

   _____

   _____

4. *through;* prepositional phrase

   _____

   _____

   _____

5. *from;* prepositional phrase

   _____

_____

_____

6. *have been restored;* verb phrase

_____

_____

_____

7. *was complicating;* verb phrase

_____

_____

_____

8. *except;* prepositional phrase

_____

_____

_____

9. *officer;* noun phrase

_____

_____

_____

10. *illuminate;* verb phrase

_____

_____

_____

11. *coursed;* participial phrase

_____

_____

_____

12. *refuge;* noun phrase

_____

_____

_____

13. *treasure;* verb phrase

_____

_____

_____

14. *changing;* gerund phrase as object of preposition

_____

_____

_____

15. *to divide;* infinitive phrase

_____

_____

_____

16. *trust;* verb phrase

_____

_____

_____

17. *below;* prepositional phrase

_____

_____

_____

18. *coat;* noun phrase

_____

_____

_____

19. *participate;* verb phrase

_____

_____

_____

20. *defeat;* noun phrase

_____

_____

_____

2.5 Verbals and Verbal Phrases

■ *Underline verbals and verbal phrases in the following sentences. Name the verbal, its part of speech, and its function.*

EXAMPLES

Reading the map was difficult in the twilight.

gerund phrase (noun) as subject of verb was

To reach the summit the climbers scaled an icy cliff.

infinitive used as adverb to modify scaled

1. Carrying her wet shoes and a soaked newspaper, the drenched salesperson walked toward the last house on the street.

   _____

2. To annoy his opponent, the chess master gently tapped his fingers.

   _____

3. Ardent fans try to move closer to the front of the auditorium.

   _____

4. Constructed in 1885, the old house had a special charm about it.

   _____

5. Scientists have been able to find links between left-handedness and a number of diseases.

   _____

6. Trained to hunt small burrowing animals, the dachshund did not originate in Germany but in Egypt.

   _____

7. Walking to work is healthy.

   _____

8. Tempted by the smell of fresh bread, she slipped into the kitchen.

   _____

9. Trained investigators try to gather as much information as they can.

_____

10. Swinging back and forth in the soft summer night, the oil lantern produced a number of eerie shadows.

_____

11. Marvin wanted to move his library into the garage.

_____

12. The office staff begins to scatter when the owner walks in.

_____

13. Using ultrasonic techniques, doctors can detect possible birth defects.

_____

14. One purpose of the National Endowment for the Humanities is to foster an awareness of our cultural inheritance.

_____

15. Peruvian Indians may support their families by weaving colorful ponchos.

_____

16. Shrimp fishermen do not support further draining of marshes.

_____

17. A major goal of psychology is learning how emotions influence behavior.

_____

18. Archaeologists, working under strenuous conditions in the Arctic, discovered toy dolls over 500 years old.

_____

19. To enjoy television one needs a comfortable couch and a variety of snacks.

_____

20. The employees to be selected for awards must excel in sales.

_____

NAME _____

DATE _____ SCORE _____

2.6 Clauses

■ *Write whether the dependent clauses are used as nouns, adjectives, or adverbs. Remember that dependent clauses can be parts of independent clauses.*

EXAMPLES

Although the horse ran well, she placed third.   *adverb*

What the speaker said could not be heard. (dependent clause used as subject of independent clause)   *noun*

The compact car *which establishes a reputation for quality* will always have a good market.   *adjective*

1. *Whoever wants help* must remain.   _____

2. *After the Greek god Pan heard the sound of the wind whistling through reeds,* he produced his own flute.   _____

3. Ice cream, *which was first commercially made in 1786,* was first sold in New York.   _____

4. *Because wiretapping is an invasion of privacy,* it is controlled by strict regulations.   _____

5. Many plays are so bad that theatergoers leave *after the first act ends.*   _____

6. All of the young dogs *that were trained as guides* had been raised as family pets.   _____

7. The foul weather *that had been expected for a week* finally arrived.   _____

8. We will help *whichever candidate gets the nomination.*   _____

9. *Since we moved to town,* five new families have moved into our neighborhood.   _____

10. *When the young reporter arrived,* she interviewed several celebrities.   _____

11. *Whoever decides to run for president* must file a financial statement with the Federal Election Commission.   _____

12. Parents *who store poisonous chemicals in locked cabinets* are protecting their children's lives. _____

13. *When the use of ostrich feathers in fashions became popular a century ago,* many ranchers in the Southwest raised ostriches. _____

14. *Why the poet failed to complete his epic* baffles many scholars. _____

15. *Although the football team was inexperienced,* it won the state championship. _____

16. *After the furniture store was renovated,* the owner held a gigantic sale. _____

17. Preferred stocks are marketed to *whoever is willing to pay a premium for less risk.* _____

18. Travelers' checks are honored at any bank *that sells them.* _____

19. The crowd was refused admission to the rally *because the auditorium was filled.* _____

20. *How the Federal Reserve will respond to inflationary pressures* is always of great interest to Wall Street. _____

2.7 Clauses

■ *Write sentences using the following coordinating or subordinating conjunctions or conjunctive adverbs to introduce or to connect clauses.*

EXAMPLES

if; to introduce a dependent clause

If the need arises, banks can borrow money from other banks to meet their financial obligations.

and; to connect two main clauses

The yellow fruit of the palm tree is tasty, and according to some scientists, it is also nutritious.

furthermore; to connect two main clauses

Many suburban townships have their own newspapers; furthermore, these papers are often quite profitable.

1. *when;* to introduce a dependent clause

_____

_____

2. *so;* to connect two main clauses

_____

_____

3. *yet;* to connect two main clauses

_____

_____

4. *where;* to introduce a dependent clause

_____

_____

5. *moreover;* to connect two main clauses

_____

_____

6. *nevertheless;* to connect two main clauses

_____

_____

7. *whichever;* to introduce a dependent clause

_____

_____

8. *if;* to introduce a dependent clause

_____

_____

9. *as;* to introduce a dependent clause

_____

_____

10. *unless;* to introduce a dependent clause

_____

_____

42

KINDS OF SENTENCES

There are four kinds of sentences: simple, compound, complex, and compound-complex.

A **simple sentence** has one independent clause.

The President flew to Camp David. (one subject, one predicate)

The President and his advisers flew to Camp David and began work on the budget. (compound subject, compound predicate)

A **compound sentence** contains two or more independent clauses joined by a coordinating conjunction or a semicolon.

The new art show at the museum opened today, and the crowd was immense. (two independent clauses joined by *and*)

The new art show at the museum opened today; the crowd was immense. (two independent clauses joined by a semicolon)

A **complex sentence** consists of one independent clause and one or more dependent clauses.

When the new art show at the museum opened, the crowd was immense. (dependent clause and independent clause)

A **compound-complex sentence** is a compound sentence with one or more dependent clauses.

After the play ended, the curtain closed, and the audience applauded loudly. (dependent clause, independent clause, independent clause)

2.8 Kinds of Sentences

■ *Identify each of the following sentences as simple (s), compound (cd), complex (cx), or compound-complex (cd/cx).*

EXAMPLES

___S___ Bombay is the commercial center of India.

___cd___ Emergency medicine is a growing specialty, and most large hospitals have trauma centers.

___cx___ Nurseries that wholesale Christmas trees increase their off-season income.

___cd/cx___ Small pickup trucks, which are now popular in urban areas, are practical for the small business, and they outsell many larger models.

_____ 1. In 1847 Theobald Boehm designed the modern flute.

_____ 2. Near Gillette, Wyoming, the tourist may see a large herd of American bison.

_____ 3. The woman is a highly regarded critic, historian, and commentator, and she is also a faculty member at the university.

_____ 4. Moving south through Vermont, New Hampshire, Massachusetts, and Connecticut, the Connecticut River reaches the Atlantic Ocean.

_____ 5. Some statements in the affidavit proved incorrect.

_____ 6. The beauty of writing lies not in how many words we know, but in the way we choose the words we use and how we organize them.

_____ 7. An object very similar to the modern bicycle is depicted in the wall art of ancient Egypt.

_____ 8. As Tom drove to his office, he sensed that he had left something important at home.

_____ 9. The water in the salt marshes along the southern Atlantic coast is replenished by the rising ocean tide.

_____ 10. Water pressure on fallen trees or on bridge pilings may be tremendous, and there may be little white water to warn a canoeist of the danger.

Sentence Errors

3

Common Sentence Errors

SENTENCE FRAGMENTS

Sentence fragments are incomplete sentences and usually consist of dependent clauses, phrases, or any other word group that does not make a complete thought. Fragments should be corrected by making the sentence complete.

NOT
The car being old. (sentence fragment: noun and phrase)
We bought a new one. (complete sentence)

BUT
The car being old, we bought a new one.

COMMA SPLICES

A **comma splice** occurs when two independent clauses are joined by a comma but have no coordinating conjunction (*and, or, nor, but, for, yet, so*).

NOT
The move was very exciting, we discussed it as we drove home.

BUT
The movie was very exciting, *and* we discussed it as we drove home.

OR
The movie was very exciting; we discussed it as we drove home.

FUSED SENTENCES

A **fused sentence** occurs when two independent clauses have neither punctuation nor a conjunction between them.

NOT
He did not heed the warning he was not very careful.

BUT
He did not heed the warning, and he was not very careful.

Fused sentences also may be corrected by writing two sentences, by using either a semicolon or a comma and a conjunction, or by making one of the sentences into a dependent clause.

He did not heed the warning. He was not very careful. (two sentences)

He did not heed the warning; he was not very careful. (semicolon)

Because he was not careful, he did not heed the warning. (dependent clause)

Both comma splices and fused sentences are often called **run-on sentences.**

3.1   Sentence Fragments

■ *In the blanks at the right identify the following as complete sentences or as fragments.*

EXAMPLES
Tune-ups save gas.

sentence

Because engines run more efficiently.

fragment

Snowdrifts are deep.

sentence

And the snow continues to fall.

sentence

1. Coming home late at night. _____

   Only to find her keys misplaced. _____

2. After the dinner dance. _____

   The band members packed their instruments. _____

3. Seals cavorting close to shore. _____

   Not noticing a nearby shark. _____

4. Spring flowers covered the field. _____

   Almost dancing in the breeze. _____

5. Light filtered through the curtains. _____

   Dust particles swirled about the room. _____

6. The rear tires being flat. _____

   We called a garage. _____

7. Quoting a famous American statesman. _____

   The candidate then referred to his own plans. _____

8. The type was too small. _____

   The ink was blurred. _____

9. To see the parade. _____

The bands and the floats. _____

10. Being quiet people. _____

Rarely object to anything. _____

4

Verb Forms

VERBS

All verbs have three principal parts:

the **infinitive** (*concern*)
the **past tense** (*concerned*)
the **past participle** (*concerned*)

These three forms are listed in the dictionary entry of each irregular verb.

Regular, Irregular Verbs

Verbs may be regular or irregular in form. **Regular verbs** (*add, help*) form the past tense and the past participle by adding -*d*, -*ed*, or sometimes -*t* (*kept, dreamt*). The principal parts of *add* and *help* are *add, added, added; help, helped, helped*.

Irregular verbs change form in the past tense and the past participle. Some irregular verbs (*begin, sing*) form the past tense and the past participle by changing a single vowel (*sing, sang, sung*). Other irregular verbs change more than one letter (*drive, drove, driven*).

Transitive, Intransitive Verbs

Verbs also may be **transitive** (take an object) or **intransitive** (do not take an object).

TRANSITIVE VERB
The cook *tasted* the special *sauce*. (*Sauce* is the direct object.)

INTRANSITIVE VERB
The rain *fell* on the roof. (*Fell* does not take an object.)

Especially troublesome are the irregular verbs *lie, lay; sit, set; rise, raise*. The verbs *lay, set,* and *raise* are transitive and take an object. The verbs *lie, sit,* and *rise* are intransitive and do not take an object.

Each of these verbs has a specific meaning. *Lie* means to recline or to be situated; *lay*, to place. *Sit* means to be seated; *set*, to place or arrange. *Rise* means to get up; *raise* means to lift. When trying to decide upon the correct form of the verb, think of the meaning you want, whether the verb takes an object or not, the tense you need, and the correct principal part. (See also pp. 69–70.)

EXAMPLES

She *lays* the book on the table. (present tense of *lay*)

She *laid* the book on the table and left. (past tense of *lay*)

The boat *lies* in the harbor. (present tense of *lie*)

The boat *lay* in the harbor most of last week. (past tense of *lie*)

The waiter *set* the plate on the table. (*Plate* is the direct object.)

The archeologist *laid* the relics taken from the temple on the examining table. (*Relics* is the direct object.)

The honor guard will *raise* the flag. (*Flag* is the direct object.)

Some of the swimmers were *lying* on the beach. (*Lying* is intransitive and takes no object.)

The sewing basket was *sitting* in the corner. (*Sitting* is intransitive and takes no object.)

The speaker *rises* to address the meeting. (*Rises* is intransitive and takes no object.)

The principal parts of these verbs are included in the following list of difficult verbs.

Principal Parts of Some Troublesome Verbs

INFINITIVE	PAST TENSE	PAST PARTICIPLE
arise	arose	arisen
awake	awoke, awaked	awoke, awaked
be	was	been
bear (to carry)	bore	borne
bear (to give birth)	bore	born, borne
begin	began	begun
bid (offer)	bid	bid
bid (order or say)	bade	bidden
bite	bit	bitten, bit
blow	blew	blown
break	broke	broken
bring	brought	brought
burst	burst	burst
catch	caught	caught
choose	chose	chosen
come	came	come
deal	dealt	dealt
dig	dug	dug
dive	dived, dove	dived
do	did	done
drag	dragged	dragged
draw	drew	drawn
dream	dreamed, dreamt	dreamed, dreamt
drink	drank	drunk
drive	drove	driven
drown	drowned	drowned
eat	ate	eaten
fall	fell	fallen

INFINITIVE	PAST TENSE	PAST PARTICIPLE
find	found	found
flee	fled	fled
fly	flew	flown
forget	forgot	forgotten, forgot
freeze	froze	frozen
get	got	got, gotten
give	gave	given
go	went	gone
grow	grew	grown
hang (to execute)	hanged	hanged
hang (to suspend)	hung	hung
have	had	had
hear	heard	heard
know	knew	known
lay	laid	laid
lead	led	led
lend	lent	lent
let	let	let
lie	lay	lain
light	lighted, lit	lighted, lit
lose	lost	lost
pay	paid	paid
pay (ropes)	payed	payed
plead	pleaded, pled	pleaded, pled
prove	proved	proven, proved
raise	raised	raised
ride	rode	ridden
ring	rang, rung	rung
rise	rose	risen
run	ran	run
say	said	said
see	saw	seen
set	set	set
shine (to give light)	shone	shone
shine (to polish)	shined	shined
show	showed	shown, showed
shrink	shrank, shrunk	shrunk
sing	sang, sung	sung
sink	sank, sunk	sunk
sit	sat	sat
slide	slid	slid
sow	sowed	sown, sowed
speak	spoke	spoken
spit	spat, spit	spit, spat
spring	sprang, sprung	sprung
stand	stood	stood
steal	stole	stolen
stink	stank, stunk	stunk
swim	swam, swum	swum
swing	swung	swung
take	took	taken
tear	tore	torn

4.1 Verb Forms

■ *Circle the correct verb form. Remember that intransitive verbs do not take direct objects. Remember that transitive verbs do take direct objects. Look for both the meaning and tense of the verb.*

EXAMPLES

The drum major (laid, lied) her baton on the ground. (The verb *laid* [past tense of *lay*] is transitive and takes the direct object *baton*.)

The wind has (rose, risen) and the leaves have (flew, flown) everywhere. (*Risen* and *flown* are intransitive; they have no direct objects.)

She (swam, swimmed) the 100-meter freestyle.

1. The company account's report (lay, laid) on the table ready for the auditor's examination.

2. The limp flag (hung, hanged) from the pole.

3. Many are (took, taken) aback by his brashness.

4. Historians continue to write about the suffering that was (born, borne) by pioneers who were part of the settling of the West.

5. The glass collection was (shown, showed) at the museum.

6. Bobcats often (sit, set) in high places to observe their territories in safety.

7. Until the storm subsided and the sea became calm, all passengers had (laid, lain) in their berths.

8. The hitter chose to (lay, lie) the bat on his shoulder and hope for a walk.

9. Animals often (sit, set) in mud to cool their dry skin and to protect themselves from insects.

10. Ships at sea (raise, rise) flags for communication.

4.2 Verb Forms

■ *Circle the correct verb form.*

EXAMPLE
Retrieving the morning newspaper, the excited dog unintentionally (tore, torn) several pages.

1. Catching the terrified faces of each figure, Goya (froze, frozed) a brutal moment in his country's history in a memorable painting.

2. The new telephone no longer (rang, rung), but made an annoying chirping noise.

3. During the presidential election campaign of 1952, several dissenting groups split from the Democratic Party.

4. A combination of dry grass, strong winds, and electrical storms or human carelessness has caused brush fires that have (rage, raged) for weeks.

5. People who lack ambition often wake up one day and realize that they have (sleeped, slept) away the best parts of their lives.

6. The candidate (begun, began) the campaign for Congress with an old-fashioned fish fry.

7. It was obvious that the jewelry was (stole, stolen).

8. The rock (slided, slid) down the mountain.

9. The book (laid, lay, lain) on the table for several days.

10. To prevent pipes from (busting, bursting) on wintry nights, one should turn on outside spigots.

4.3 Verb Forms

■ *Circle the correct verb form.*

EXAMPLE

The cotton uniforms had ((shrunk,) shrank) in the wash before the team wore them.

1. The price of meat has (rised, risen) considerably in the past few years.

2. A familiar sight in most American homes on Sunday mornings is parts of the newspaper (lying, laying) all over the floor.

3. Complaints about the unhealthy working conditions in the plant were (writed, written) down by the employees and submitted to the section manager.

4. When we tried out the appliance that we ordered through a television commercial, nothing (seem, seemed) to work right.

5. The cowboys on the cattle drive had (rode, ridden) over 400 miles.

6. Donkeys have been known to (bore, bear) twice their weight on their exceptionally strong backs.

7. The school board (came, come) to no decision on the issue of attendance regulations.

8. A newly discovered Roman vessel (sanked, sank) off the coast of Sicily sometime during the third century B.C.

9. (Rang, Rung) only twice, the Liberty Bell now sits in Independence Hall in Philadelphia.

10. The trustees of the estate (paid, payed) all bills before disbursing legacies to the surviving relations.

TENSE AND SEQUENCE OF TENSES

Use verbs carefully to express distinctions of time. Avoid needless shifts of tense.

Usually the **present tense** expresses present time.

I *am going* home for lunch.

It also may show repeated action.

I *go* home for lunch.

The **past tense** shows past time.

I *went* home for lunch.
I *lay* in the sun for an hour. (past tense of verb *lie*)

The **future tense** shows future time.

I *shall go* home for lunch.

Perfect Tenses

The three perfect tenses are used in well-defined sequences. They indicate time or action completed before another time or action.

1. Use **present perfect** with present.

I *have asked* her to help, and she *refuses.*

2. Use **past perfect** with past.

He *had wanted* to diet, but he *could* not.

3. Use **future perfect** with future.

He *will have finished* before we *will begin*.

Infinitive

An infinitive usually takes the present tense when it expresses action that occurs at the same time as that of the controlling verb.

I *desired* to leave.
To *complete* the project, we *had* to work overtime yesterday.

Relationships between verbs should be logical and consistent.

NOT

I *walk* to the park and *had* lunch. (mixes present tense and past tense)

BUT

I *walked* to the park and *had* lunch. (past tense with past tense)

VOICE

When the subject acts, the verb is in the **active voice.** When the subject is acted upon, the verb is in the **passive voice.** Passive voice may lead to wordiness and can be confusing because it omits the doer of the action.

ACTIVE VOICE
Bill *gave* the book to Mary. (*Bill* acts.)

PASSIVE VOICE
The *book* was given to Mary. (*Book* is acted upon.)

SUBJUNCTIVE MOOD

Use the **subjunctive mood** to show wishes, commands, or conditions contrary to fact.

I wish I *were* rich. (wish)

The rules require that we *be* silent. (command)

If I *were* vacationing this week, I would be a happy person. (condition contrary to fact)

5

Agreement: Subject and Verb

Use singular verbs with singular subjects, and use plural verbs with plural subjects. The *-s* or *-es* ending of the present tense of a verb in the third person (*he hopes, she stops*) indicates the singular. For most nouns, however, these same endings indicate the plural.

After Compound Subject

A **compound subject** with *and* usually takes a plural verb.

The city *and* the county *are* working together.

Collective Nouns

Collective nouns (words like *family, flock, jury*) take a singular verb when referring to a group as a unit; they take a plural verb when the members of a group are treated individually.

My *family is* going on a trip this weekend.
My *family are* going to Hawaii, New Jersey, and Ohio on Labor Day.

After Relative Pronoun

After a relative pronoun (such as *who, which,* and *that*), the verb in the relative clause has the same person and number as the *antecedent* of the pronoun.

The sales *associate* who *is* here today represents a well-known firm.

After Titles

A title of a book or film is singular and requires a singular verb, even if it contains plural words and ideas.

Elements of Films is a useful book.

After *There, Here*

In sentences that begin with *there* and *here,* the verb agrees with the subject of the sentence.

There *is* an old *mill* on this road. (*Mill* is the subject.)
There *are* many *challenges* in this project. (*Challenges* is the subject.)

Word Groups

Word groups, such as *in addition to* and *as well as*, do not change the number of the subject when they separate the subject and the verb.

State *officials as well as* our mayor *are examining* the problem.

The Subject

The *subject* of the sentence, not the predicate noun, determines the number of the verb.

Her main *strength is* her ability to listen and to follow instructions.

When the subject in a sentence is *inverted*, the verb should agree with the *subject* of the sentence, not with the word that comes directly before the verb.

At the party *were Beatrice* and her *sister*. (Plural verb agrees with compound subject.)

NAME _____

DATE _____ SCORE _____

5.1 Subject and Verb Agreement

■ *Underline each subject once; then write the correct verb in the blank at the right.*

EXAMPLES
The fall <u>colors</u> and cool <u>evenings</u> (make, makes) our vacation to the mountains very enjoyable.

make

<u>Either</u> geology or biology (satisfies, satisfy) the science requirement.

satisfies

1. Auto manufacturers recall thousands of cars each year because they discover that there (are, is) a major defect that could cause an accident.

_____

2. Interesting conversation (enliven, enlivens) a party.

_____

3. Visiting national parks and driving through small towns that are off main highways (is, are) favorite types of vacations for many people.

_____

4. Neither reports nor debates at board meetings (convince, convinces) all directors to vote with management.

_____

5. There (come, comes) a time when everyone must think about retirement.

_____

6. A large crowd of people (was, were) at the sports arena.

_____

7. We like everyone who (live, lives) in our neighborhood.

_____

8. The convocation speaker as well as his wife and children (was, were) welcomed heartily by the audience.

_____

9. We really (was, were) impressed with the day-care centers.

_____

10. There (is, are) many Americans who never bother to vote.

_____

5.2 Subject and Verb Agreement

■ *Underline each subject once; then write the correct verb in the blank at the right.*

EXAMPLES

All <u>members</u> of the council (is, are) present. *are*

<u>Everyone</u> (is, are) here for the presentation of the awards. *is*

1. Auto insurance policies (has been, have been) changed to provide greater coverage. _____

2. A workshop as well as individual instruction (was, were) planned. _____

3. The majority of public officials (is, are) dedicated to their work. _____

4. Both vegetables and flowers (grows, grow) in our garden. _____

5. Whoever (say, says) the new statue in the park is ugly is making an understatement. _____

6. The Science Club, which is sponsored by the Physics Department, (participate, participates) in the state Science Fair this weekend. _____

7. On the list of bowlers in the tournament (was, were) Mary Ashley, Sonja Taylor, and Ruthie Johns, clearly the best in the region. _____

8. The mural, viewed at the shopping center by the opening-day crowd, (was, were) shocking to many. _____

9. The desire to economize and help solve the energy shortage (sell, sells) many subcompact automobiles. _____

10. Students' lack of desire to learn (cause, causes) teachers many heartaches. _____

6

Pronouns: Agreement and Reference

ANTECEDENTS

Use singular pronouns to refer to singular antecedents, and use plural pronouns to refer to plural antecedents. Use a plural pronoun to refer to compound antecedents, except in those cases where the antecedents refer to the same person.

The *instructor* finished grading *her* papers.
The *instructors* finished grading *their* papers.

Which and *that* refer to animals and things. *Who* refers to people and rarely to animals and things called by name. *That* refers to animals and things, but only occasionally to people.

The refrigerator *that (which)* I bought never needs defrosting.
The representative *who* sold it to me guaranteed the unit for ten years.

Pronouns should not refer vaguely to an entire sentence or to unidentified people. Do not make vague references using pronouns *they, them, it, you, this,* or *which*.

I have trouble taking standardized tests. *This* is my problem. (*This* is too vague.)
You know that *they* will do *it* every time. (*You, they,* and *it* are vague references.)

Make a pronoun refer clearly to one antecedent only.

UNCERTAIN
The man went to the doctor after *he* finished work. (Does *he* refer to *doctor* or *man?*)

CLEAR
After *he* finished work, the man went to the doctor. (*He* now clearly refers to *man.*)

CORRECT CASE

Pronouns have three cases: subjective, possessive, and objective. Personal pronouns and the relative pronoun *who* are inflected for these cases.

Subjective (acting)—I, he, she, we, they, who, you, it

Possessive (possessing)—my (mine), your (yours), his, her (hers), its, our (ours), their (theirs), whose

Objective (acted upon)—me, him, her, us, them, one, whom, you, it

To determine case, find out how a word is used in its own clause—for example, whether it is a subject, a subjective complement, a possessive, or an object.

Use the **subjective case** for subjects and subjective complements.

SUBJECT
The contractor and *I* are about to reach an agreement. (Use *I*, not *me*, for the subject.)

SUBJECTIVE COMPLEMENT (OR PREDICATE NOMINATIVE)
The winner was *I*. (Use *I*, not *me*, after a linking verb.)

Use the **possessive case** to show ownership and with gerunds.

Their work was complete. (ownership)

Her rising to the presidency reflected hard work. (gerund)

The possessive forms of personal pronouns do *not* have apostrophes.

His is the best solution.

The possessive forms of indefinite pronouns (*everybody's, one's, anyone's*) do have apostrophes. Contractions such as *it's* (for *it is*) and *she's* (for *she is*) do have apostrophes.

Also use the **objective case** for the object of a preposition and for the subject of an infinitive.

Who among *us* will volunteer? (*Us* is the object of *among*.)

The college selected *her* to be the coach. (*Her* is the subject of the infinitive *to be*.)

For Interrogative Pronouns

The case of interrogatives (*who, whose, whom, what, which* used in questions) depends on their use in a specific clause.

Whom did the Senate confirm for the post? (Use *whom*, not *who*, because the interrogative pronoun is a direct object of *did confirm*.)

For Appositives

For pronouns used as **appositives** (words that rename nouns or pronouns) use the same case as the noun or pronoun renamed.

Only we—Sharon and I—were excused. (*Sharon* and *I* rename the subject *we;* hence, use *I*, not *me*.)

The instructor excused two of us, Sharon and *me*. (*Sharon* and *me* rename the object of the preposition *of;* hence, use the objective case.)

After *Than, As*

The correct case of a pronoun used after *than* or *as* is determined by completing the missing verb of the clause:

Margaret is taller than I. (*Than I am* is the complete clause; *I* is the subject of the clause.)

She worked harder than you or I. (*than you or I worked*)

This crisis hurt him more than her. (*more than it hurt her; her* is the object)

6.1 Pronouns: Agreement and Reference

■ *In the following sentences choose the correct pronouns and write them in the blanks at the right.*

EXAMPLES

The company plans to extend insurance benefits to all of (its, their) employees.   *its*

County maps are useful for census-takers as (they, he or she) attempt to reach all households.   *they*

1. Her paintings hung in several major museums because (it, they) were so good.   _____

2. Freight trains were called *rattlers* in the 1840s because (it, they) made so much noise.   _____

3. The new marketing concept is promising, but (they, it) lacks sufficient planning.   _____

4. Those (who, that) saw the accident gave different accounts of the cause.   _____

5. People often accidentally find (themself, themselves) on a street that is dark and foreboding.   _____

6. Keeping (its, their) budget under control, the company was able to save several thousand dollars.   _____

7. Dana Morey and her assistants are turning (her, their) attention to more radical architectural designs.   _____

8. People who swim without supervision endanger (one's life, their lives).   _____

9. Large corporations in the United States (who, which) do international business value college graduates with a knowledge of foreign languages.   _____

10. Many researchers are now studying the causes of failure to find ways to prevent (it, them).   _____

6.3 Case

■ *Write the correct case form in the following sentences in the blanks at the right.*

EXAMPLES
(Whoever, Whomever) invented the wheel deserves the gratitude of everyone.

Whoever

(subject of verb *invented*)

About (whom, who) are you speaking?

whom

(object of preposition *about*)

1. The contracts went to those (who, whom) had made the lowest bids.   _____

2. Tom, Dick, and (I, me) have trouble passing organic chemistry tests.   _____

3. It was a pleasure to see (they, them) working hard for a change.   _____

4. Flight attendants help passengers find (them, their) seats and store their small luggage.   _____

5. The race was nearly a tie, and (who, whom) won it was difficult to determine.   _____

6. The president gave (us, we) three special awards at the annual sales meeting.   _____

7. No other typist in the class can type as rapidly as (he, him).   _____

8. The band members asked (themselves, theirselves) what had gone wrong during the rehearsal.   _____

9. We knew (her, she) to be loyal to her principles.   _____

10. He dedicated his book to (whoever, whomever) cherished liberty.   _____

NAME _____

DATE _____ SCORE _____

6.4 Case

■ *Write the correct case form in the following sentences in the blanks at the right.*

EXAMPLE
(Their, Them) singing is delightful.

Their

(possessive case with gerund)

1. Rachael told (who, whom) our secret? _____

2. The beef served at the new restaurant was tougher than (we, us) expected. _____

3. The jigsaw puzzle took two of us, Jeff and (I, me), to put it together. _____

4. Our teacher thought that Ann and (I, me) were always in trouble. _____

5. Several tendons in (my, mine) leg were injured in the fall. _____

6. (Who, Whom) did the publisher decide to choose as the new editor? _____

7. Many Americans complain that (we, us) taxpayers must pay too much money to the government. _____

8. We helped more than (they, them), but they received more credit. _____

9. The governor traveled to France with my wife and (I, me) to celebrate Bastille Day. _____

10. (Whoever, Whomever) owns the disputed land near the present borders of Wyoming and Colorado may be wealthy some day. _____

NAME _____

DATE _____ SCORE _____

6.5 Case

■ *Write the correct case form in the following sentences in the blank at the right.*

EXAMPLE
The champions were Doug and (I, me).   _____I_____

1. (We, Us) four were on the social committee for our club.   _____

2. My employer was as pleased as (I, me) when I entered the training program for computer operators.   _____

3. I have great regard for (whomever, whoever) can repair watches.   _____

4. The truck driver asked (me, I) for directions to the new industrial park.   _____

5. The candidate for the state house proclaimed, "It is (we, us) the people who must chart a new course for state government."   _____

6. Everyone was pleased at (him, his) coming to the party.   _____

7. The chef said, "It is (I, me) who baked the bread."   _____

8. When the investigation of the fire began, the experts were able to determine (who, whom) caused it.   _____

9. "Can anyone tell me (who, whom) our twenty-third President was?" the historian asked.   _____

10. "The last of (we, us) to leave should lock the doors," the librarian said.   _____

7

Adjective or Adverb?

ADJECTIVES AND ADVERBS COMPARED

Adjectives modify nouns and pronouns. **Adverbs** modify verbs, adjectives, and other adverbs.

The bright light hurt *our* eyes. (*The* and *bright* are adjectives modifying *light*, and *our* is a possessive adjective modifying *eyes*.)

The news spread *quickly*. (*Quickly* is an adverb modifying *spread*.)

Most adverbs end in *-ly*. Only a few adjectives (*lovely, friendly,* for example) have this ending. Some adverbs have two forms, one with *-ly* and one without (*closely, close* and *quickly, quick*). Most adverbs are formed by adding *-ly* to adjectives (*sudden, suddenly* and *hasty, hastily*.)

We had an *easy* choice to make. (*Easy* is an adjective.)

We made the choice *easily*. (*Easily* is an adverb.)

Use a predicate adjective, not an adverb, after a linking verb, such as *be, become, seem, look, appear, feel, sound, smell, taste*.

The *meat* tastes *bad*. (*Bad* describes the *meat*.)

The *actress* felt *calm*. (*Calm* describes the *actress*.)

One feels *good* after finishing a long swim. (*Good* describes how one feels.)

BUT

The gymnast performed *well*. (The adverb *well* modifies the verb *performed*.)

FORMS OF THE COMPARATIVE AND SUPERLATIVE

Use the **comparative form** of the adjective to refer to two things; use the *superlative form* to refer to more than two. Add *-er* or *-est* to form the comparative and the superlative of most short modifiers.

The new air terminal is much *larger* than the old one.

Of the five hotels in our city, the *newest* one is the *largest*.

Use *more* or *most* (or *less* or *least*) rather than *-er* and *-est* before long modifiers, that is, modifiers of several syllables.

She is *more capable* than her sister (not *capabler*)

She is the *most capable* person I know. (not *capablest*)

He is very *fast*. (predicate adjective)

He is *faster* than his brother. (comparative form)

He is the *fastest* runner in our class. (superlative form)

Some adjectives and adverbs have irregular comparative and superlative forms:

good, better, best; bad, worse, worst

7.1 Adjective or Adverb?

■ *Write the correct form of adjective or adverb in the blank at the right.*

EXAMPLES

A (high, highly) productive honeybee hive is fascinating. *highly*

(adverb *highly* modifies adjective *productive*)

(Slight, Slightly) sunlight is enough for this fern. *Slight*

(adjective *slight* modifies noun *sunlight*)

1. The work went (well, good) after the construction crew was enlarged. _____

2. We will follow the progress of the space flight (close, closely). _____

3. Most wild animals fight (vicious, viciously) when they are cornered. _____

4. People often eat too (quick, quickly) so they can watch television. _____

5. Before the meetings began, the members of the trade commission from England were greeted very (warm, warmly). _____

6. After deciding which college to attend, she felt (good, well) about her decision. _____

7. Every applicant performed (good, well) on the tests. _____

8. Mail may be delayed (frequent, frequently) by bad weather. _____

9. The plain before the pioneers was (vast, vastly) and covered with wildflowers. _____

10. (Really, Real) good ice cream is now available in over fifty flavors and at a reasonable cost. _____

11. Teams that remain (close, closely) are usually very successful. _____

12. The fresh cookies went (quick, quickly). _____

13. The newscaster told the anxious audience that the rescue was going as (good, well) as could be expected.

_____

14. The Western Hemisphere has two of the world's (larger, largest) rivers, the Amazon and the Mississippi; of the two, the Amazon is the (larger, largest), but the Mississippi is the (most, more) important economically.

_____

_____

15. Once on the endangered species list, the American alligator is now (abundant, abundantly) because of (more strict, stricter) law enforcement and better game management.

_____

_____

16. The economists found it was not (possible, possibly) for them to predict interest rates.

_____

17. Of all the space walks, Armstrong's was the (better, best).

_____

18. The stock cars passed the stands so (rapidly, rapid) that it was impossible to tell (accurate, accurately) who was ahead.

_____

_____

19. Being (solid, solidly) behind the new housing program, the young politicians had to fight opponents who were (strong, strongly) opposed to them.

_____

_____

20. Most conductors are (usual, usually) pleased with requests for encores.

_____

7.2 Adjective or Adverb?

■ *Write the correct forms of adjectives or adverbs in the blanks at the right.*

EXAMPLES
The cake looks (good, well).

good

(adjective *good* after linking verb

Our track team performed (good, well).

well

(adverb *well* modifies verb *performed*)

1. Spelunkers must crawl (cautious, cautiously) through caves.   _____

2. Of the eight girls in our class, the (smaller, smallest) was the brightest.   _____

3. (Normal, Normally) many employees expect to leave early on Friday.   _____

4. The physician treated the wound with (careful, carefully), methodical steps.   _____

5. The extra work caused by the reduction in the department's staff fell (heavy, heavily) on the shoulders of four employees.   _____

6. Trent tried to complete his homework as (quick, quickly) as possible.   _____

7. "If you want a (real, really) effective stereo that   _____
   plays music (clear, clearly)," the clerk advised,
   "we'll sell you a graphic equalizer."   _____

8. After the relay race, the losing team looked   _____
   (glum, glumly) and said that they felt (worse,
   worst, worser, badder) than they looked.   _____

9. As the cowboy (careful, carefully) put his cup of very thick coffee down, he remarked to the waitress, "One thing about your coffee: it sure ain't scared."   _____

10. Because the waitress scowled, the cowboy became more (careful, carefully) when he spoke.   _____

Sentence Structure

8

Coordination, Subordination, Completeness, Comparisons, Consistency

Linking a number of short dependent clauses and sentences produces wordiness and monotony and fails to show precise relationships between thoughts.

EXAMPLE

The United States has changed significantly in the last fifty years, for the life expectancy of Americans has increased ten years for men and fifteen years for women, and the nation's work force has quadrupled.

IMPROVED

The United States has changed significantly in the last fifty years. The life expectancy of Americans has increased ten years for men and fifteen years for women. In addition, the nation's work force has quadrupled.

SUBORDINATION

Use subsordinate clauses accurately and effectively to avoid excessive coordination and to achieve variety and emphasis. However, avoid excessive subordination, which may ruin style or create excessively long sentences.

EXCESSIVE SUBORDINATION

My grandfather took great pleasure throughout his life in the craft of carving wooden figures, which he learned to do when he was young, which was a time when people did not have the great number of amusements which we have today.

BETTER

My grandfather, who lived in a time when people did not have the great number of amusements of today, learned when young to carve wooden figures. He took great pleasure in the craft throughout his life.

Express main ideas in independent clauses; express less important ideas in subordinate clauses.

IMPROPER SUBORDINATION

Few people know that he got his seed from mills that made apple cider, although Johnny Appleseed became famous for planting apple trees throughout the Ohio Valley.

BETTER

Although few people know that he got his seed from mills that made apple cider, Johnny Appleseed became famous for planting apple trees throughout the Ohio Valley.

Avoid excessive overlapping of subordinate clauses. A series of clauses with each one depending on the previous one is confusing.

OVERLAPPING SUBORDINATION
The United States Treasury Department, which is located in Washington, which is responsible for the printing and minting of currency, is also responsible for the protection of the President.

IMPROVED
Located in Washington, the United States Treasury Department is responsible for the printing and minting of currency and for the protection of the President.

COMPLETENESS

After *So, Such, Too*

Make your sentences complete in structure and thought, especially sentences with *so*, *such*, and *too*.

NOT CLEAR
The house was so hot. (so hot that something must have happened)

CLEAR
The house was so hot that we had to turn on the air conditioner.

NOT CLEAR
The room was in such confusion. (What happened?)

CLEAR
The room was in such confusion that we could not find the telephone book.

Omission of Verbs and Prepositions

Do not omit a verb or a preposition that is necessary to the structure of the sentence.

NOT
We were interested and then bored by the lecture.

BUT
We were interested in and then bored by the lecture.

NOT
The passengers were impatient and the plane late.

BUT
The passengers were impatient, and the plane was late.

Omission of *That*

The omission of *that* is often confusing.

INCOMPLETE
He was grieved she did not love him.

He was grieved that she did not love him.

COMPARISONS

Make comparisons clear and complete by comparing only similar terms, using the word *other* where necessary, and avoiding awkward and incomplete comparisons.

INCORRECT
The bite of a person is often worse than a dog.

LOGICAL
The bite of a person is often worse than the bite of a dog.

INCORRECT
The Grand Canyon is larger than any canyon in the world.

LOGICAL
The Grand Canyon is larger than any other canyon in the world.

INCORRECT
Reading is one of the most pleasant if not the most pleasant pastime one can enjoy. (After *one of the most pleasant*, the plural *pastimes* is required.)

BETTER
Reading is one of the most pleasant pastimes one can enjoy, if not the most pleasant.

OR
Reading is one of the most pleasant pastimes.

Avoid ambiguous comparisons.

AMBIGUOUS
We enjoyed visiting the city more than our parents. (*More* than visiting parents, or *more* than the parents enjoyed the city?)

CLEAR
We enjoyed visiting the city more than our parents did.

CONSISTENCY

Avoid confusing shifts in grammatical forms.

Shifts in Tense

INCORRECT
The doctor was well trained, but his patients are dissatisfied.

CORRECT
The doctor is well trained, but his patients are dissatisfied.

Shifts in Person

INCORRECT
When we left our hotel, you could see the capitol building.

CORRECT
When we left our hotel, we could see the capitol building.

Shifts in Number

INCORRECT
A person may decide on their vocation late in life.

CORRECT
People may decide on their vocations late in life.

Shifts in Voice

INCORRECT
The assignment *is read* by the student, and then she *answers* the questions at the end of the chapter.

CORRECT
The student *reads* the assignment, and then she *answers* the questions at the end of the chapter. (Put both parts of the sentence in the active voice.)

9. Flamingos are large birds which wade in search of food and have red or pink plumage and have long legs, long necks, and a bill that turns downward at the tip.

_____

_____

_____

_____

10. A justice of the peace is a magistrate at the lowest level of a state's court system who performs marriages, who administers oaths, and who usually acts upon minor offenses that otherwise would crowd the dockets of higher courts.

_____

_____

_____

_____

8.4 Completeness and Comparisons

■ *Revise the following sentences to correct any errors in completeness and comparisons.*

EXAMPLES

The colonel was too old.

The colonel was too old to be an astronaut.

Rafting on the Colorado River is more exciting than any river in the United States.

Rafting on the Colorado River is more exciting than rafting on any other river in the United States.

1. Brad was happier this year.

_____

_____

2. Modern jetliners are different.

_____

_____

3. The aircraft flying over the neighborhood have and continue to annoy residents.

_____

_____

_____

4. Joyce thinks her new pickup truck is better.

_____

_____

_____

5. The new draperies cost me more than my mother.

_____

_____

_____

6. Forgetting a school assignment is worse than any mistake in school.

_____

_____

_____

7. The tenant in the apartment was both interested and suspicious of his neighbor.

_____

_____

_____

8. The new investigative reporter was as good if not better than some of the older reporters.

_____

_____

_____

9. The new play at our local theater is one of the most interesting if not the most interesting this season.

_____

_____

_____

10. My date liked me better than my friend Jane.

_____

_____

_____

8.5 Completeness and Comparisons

■ *Revise the following sentences to correct any errors in completeness and comparisons.*

EXAMPLE
No one works harder.

No one works harder than John.

1. In many cases laser surgery is more efficient.

_____

_____

_____

2. The library staff worked harder this year.

_____

_____

_____

3. Many children understand their personal problems better.

_____

_____

_____

4. A completely rebuilt engine is usually just as dependable.

_____

_____

_____

5. My stereo system produces better sound than Tom.

_____

_____

_____

6. The lawyer was both involved and concerned about the trial's outcome.

   _____

   _____

   _____

7. For children simple building blocks are as enjoyable if not more enjoyable than more expensive toys.

   _____

   _____

   _____

8. The new business regulations are both examples and guides to the administration's traditional economic policies.

   _____

   _____

   _____

9. The clerk had never and never would be eligible for a long vacation because he took so many days off during the year.

   _____

   _____

   _____

10. Sri Lanka, formerly Ceylon, has and continues to be the world's chief supplier of natural cinnamon.

    _____

    _____

    _____

8.6 Consistency

■ *Revise the following sentences making them structurally consistent. Avoid unnecessary shifts in tense, person, mood, or voice and shifts from one relative pronoun to another.*

EXAMPLES

Abraham Lincoln was only fifty-two when he becomes the sixteenth President of the United States.

Abraham Lincoln was only fifty-two when he became the sixteenth President of the United States.

(revised for consistency in tense)

When I traveled to the mountains of the Northwest, you can see great varieties of plant life.

When I traveled to the mountains of the Northwest, I saw great varieties of plant life.

(revised for consistency in person and tense)

1. I enjoy a cold glass of iced tea because one feels refreshed after you drink it.

_____

_____

2. Each of you have been given complete instructions, so one should not make any mistakes.

_____

_____

3. We thought the light at the end of the tunnel is a sign of hope, but it was just a train coming in our direction.

_____

_____

_____

4. Dreams are not necessarily accidental, for they often were considered efforts of the subconscious to work out real problems.

_____

_____

5. The article in the newspaper is very critical of the congressman and would have been very damaging if he chooses to run again.

_____

_____

6. The cheetah is very tired after chasing its quarry and usually rested for several minutes before it ate.

_____

_____

7. The woman discovered the real identity of her friend after she knows her for twenty years.

_____

_____

8. After we had been hiking for several days, we grow tired and stop to rest.

_____

_____

9. One of my closest friends was Larry Marconi, who is my neighbor.

_____

_____

10. The dam would have held huge amounts of water and will provide irrigation for the hundreds of farms in the nearby valley.

_____

_____

Position of Modifiers, Parallelism, Sentence Variety

MODIFIERS

Attach modifiers to the correct word or element in the sentence to avoid confusion. Most adjectives precede the noun they modify. Adverbs may come before or follow the words they modify. Prepositional phrases usually follow the word they modify, as do adjective clauses. Adverbial phrases and clauses may be placed in various positions—as decided by the writer.

EXAMPLES

The new forms are finished. (adjective before the noun)

The auditions *soon* ended. (adverb before the verb)

The auditions ended *soon*. (adverb after the verb)

The officer *on the corner* hailed a motorist. (prepositional phrase modifying *officer*)

The lady came *to the door*. (prepositional phrase modifying *came*)

Sooner than we expected, the movie ended. (adverbial clause modifying *ended*)

The movie ended *sooner than we expected*. (adverbial clause modifying *ended*)

DANGLING MODIFIERS

Avoid dangling modifiers. A verbal phrase needs a subject for its action.

Dangling Participle

Seeing the fresh apple pie, *my hunger* grew.

CLEAR
Seeing the fresh apple pie, *I* grew hungry.

Dangling Gerund

After examining my checkbook, *my error* was found.

CLEAR
After examining my checkbook, *I found* my error.

Dangling Infinitive

To get an early start, *the alarm clock* was set for 6 A.M.

CLEAR

To get an early start, *I set* the alarm clock for 6 A.M.

Dangling Prepositional Phrase

While *in school*, my mother did her shopping.

CORRECT

While *I was* in school, my mother did her shopping.

MISPLACED MODIFIERS, SQUINTING MODIFIERS

Almost any modifier that comes between an adjective clause and the word it modifies can cause confusion.

UNCLEAR

Many people are questioned by grand juries *who may be innocent*.

CLEAR

Many people *who may be innocent* are questioned by grand juries.

A modifier placed between two words so that it may modify either word is a **squinting modifier**.

UNCLEAR

The chess master who was playing *carefully* won the first game.

CLEAR

The chess master who was *carefully* playing won the first game.

SEPARATION OF ELEMENTS

Do not separate closely related elements, such as the subject and the verb, parts of a verb phrase, or a verb and an object.

AWKWARD

The construction workers *had*, for a week, *expected* a new contract.

IMPROVED

For a week, the construction workers *had expected* a new contract.

Avoid **split infinitives** (modifiers between *to* and the verb form).

NOT

to actively *pursue*

BUT

to pursue actively

PARALLELISM

Make construction in a sentence parallel (balanced) by matching phrase with phrase, clause with clause, verb with verb, and so on.

124

FAULTY

The men argued *bitterly* and *were loud*.

IMPROVED

The men argued *bitterly* and *loudly*.

Repeat an article (*a, an,* or *the*), a preposition (*by, in, for,* and so on), or other words to preserve parallelism and clarity.

FAULTY

The aircraft was *in a storm* and *trouble*.

IMPROVED

The aircraft was *in a storm* and *in trouble*.

SENTENCE VARIETY

Vary sentences in structure and order. Use loose, periodic, and balanced sentence forms.

A **loose sentence** makes its main point at the beginning of the sentence and then adds qualifications or refinements.

We left early, missing the heavy traffic.

A **periodic sentence** saves the main point until the end of a sentence to create suspense or emphasis.

After a long afternoon visiting my aunt, I was eager to go home.

A **balanced sentence** has parallel parts in terms of structure, length, and thoughts.

We must work so that we may live, not live that we may work.

9.3 Separation of Elements

■ *Do not separate closely related elements unnecessarily. Separation of parts of a verb phrase, a verb and its object, or a subject and its verb can be awkward or misleading. Revise the following sentences by correcting unnecessarily separated elements.*

EXAMPLE

The domestication of animals had, years before civilization began, become commonplace in Egypt.

The domestication of animals had become commonplace in Egypt years before civilization began.

1. Visit us, if you have the opportunity, soon.

_____

_____

_____

2. We at best knew that our taxes would increase slightly next year.

_____

_____

_____

3. After the debris was, by the Army Corp of Engineers, cleared, the stream dropped below flood stage.

_____

_____

_____

4. We wanted to easily avoid traffic.

_____

_____

_____

5. People have, after finishing late afternoon shopping, often to drive home in heavy traffic.

_____

_____

_____

6. People always need to, whenever they plan a trip, make certain the police are notified that they will be away from home.

_____

_____

_____

7. Eating in new restaurants, although it is sometimes a great mistake, is usually quite exciting.

_____

_____

_____

8. Maria, using the money she had earned as a clinical psychologist, bought the stereo equipment she had wanted for several years.

_____

_____

_____

9. Micah watched, through the living-room window, with envy as his older brother and sister left for the first day of school.

_____

_____

_____

10. There was hope that Nicole, although she had not received any information, would hear about her scholarship in a few days.

_____

_____

_____

9.7 Variety in Sentences

■ *Revise the following sentences for greatest emphasis and for the most logical or climactic order. Write C to the left of any correct sentence.*

EXAMPLE
On the legislative agenda are tax reform, billboard regulations, and new committee assignments.

On the legislative agenda are new committee assignments, billboard regulations, and tax reform.

(Revised to move from least to most important item.)

1. She won the women's amateur tennis championship six years after she started competition in the city tournaments.

2. An old car frequently fails to start, is uncomfortable, and uses too much oil.

3. The runner broke his best time, beat his opponents in the meet, and set a world record.

4. The earthquake destroyed an entire section of the city, interrupted communications, and damaged several highways.

5. The famous novelist toured several countries, won the Nobel Prize, and finished his twentieth book.

_____

_____

6. Drivers prepared themselves for delays, slowed their cars, and turned on their headlights when fog began to cover the Golden Gate Bridge.

_____

_____

_____

7. After the machinist lost her position, she was interviewed by several companies, searched the help-wanted advertisements for a new job, and wrote letters listing her qualifications.

_____

_____

_____

8. Both political candidates have previous public service; they have served in the United States Senate, on the state board of mines, and on the local school board.

_____

_____

_____

9. The river rapidly reached flood level after the dam collapsed.

_____

_____

10. We decided not to fly our small plane to Atlanta because the weather reports predicted icy conditions above 2,000 feet.

_____

_____

_____

Punctuation

The Comma

USES OF THE COMMA

Although the comma has many functions, it is used, in general, to separate elements and to set off modifiers or parenthetical elements.

Between Two Independent Clauses

Use the comma to separate independent clauses joined by a coordinating conjunction (*and*, *but*, *or*, *nor*, *for*, *so*, *yet*).

The brisk winds raised only moderate waves, *but* the falling barometer indicated stormy weather was coming.

In a Series

Use a comma between words, phrases, and clauses in a series.

We chose red, gold, and white for our color scheme. (words in a series)

The audience was seated, the overture had begun, and the curtain was about to open. (clauses in a series)

Between Coordinate Adjectives

Use a comma between **coordinate adjectives** not joined by *and*. Coordinate adjectives each modify the noun (or pronoun) independently.

The *gloomy, uninhabited* house was very isolated.

Cumulative adjectives do not modify independently. Do not use a comma between cumulative adjectives.

He discarded his *shabby old* clothes.

Note: to recognize coordinate adjectives, place the word *and* between them and determine whether they sound right.

The gloomy *and* uninhabited house was isolated. (sounds right)

He discarded his shabby *and* old clothes. (sounds wrong and is ambiguous: only shabby old clothes? shabby clothes and old clothes?)

Another test is to reverse the adjectives. Normally, coordinate adjectives are easily reversible.

uninhabited, gloomy house (sounds right)

old shabby clothes (sounds wrong)

After Long Introductory Clauses or Phrases

Use a comma after a long introductory phrase or clause.

At the end of my first full day at work, I was ready for a good dinner. (phrase)

When my first full day at work ended, I was ready for a good dinner. (clause)

Introductory verbal phrases usually are set off by a comma.

Working alone, she built a new room at the mountain retreat. (participial phrase)

To prepare for the race, the runner trained for weeks. (infinitive phrase)

After finishing dinner, we took a long walk. (prepositional phrase)

With Nonrestrictive Elements

Use commas to set off nonrestrictive appositives, phrases, and clauses that add description or information but are not essential to the meaning of the sentence.

Mary Evans, *the company comptroller*, was invited to a meeting in Washington. (nonrestrictive appositive phrase)

Mary Evans, *who is the company comptroller*, was invited to a meeting in Washington. (nonrestrictive adjective clause)

Note that a restrictive element is *never* set off by commas, because it is necessary for the meaning of the total sentence.

The music *that we most enjoy* is contemporary.

With Parenthetical Elements

Use commas with parenthetical elements

We are prepared to continue the project, *we believe*, if there is enough public interest.

With Conjunctive Adverbs

Use a comma after a conjunctive adverb (*however, nevertheless, moreover, furthermore*, and so on) when it precedes an independent clause.

The profit margin was down; *however*, next year should be better.

With Unusual Word Order

Use commas with sentence elements out of normal word order.

The trainer, *haggard and thin*, slowly saddled the horse.

With Degrees, Titles, Dates, Places, Addresses

Use commas with degrees and titles, as well as to separate elements in dates, places, and addresses.

Rosa Adams, M.D., joined the staff. (comma before and after *M.D.*)
On March 10, 1971, my daughter was born. (comma before and after year)
On Monday, December 19, the Christmas vacation begins.
Sedona, Arizona, is at the entrance to Oak Creek Canyon. (Use a comma before and after the name of a state when the city is named)

BUT

n July 1969, we bought a new home. (optional commas)
e year 1945 marked the end of World War II. (no comma)
new address is 196 Warner Avenue, Westwood, California 73520. (no a before zip code)

ast or Emphasis

for contrast and emphasis as well as for short interroga-

t, not this one.
T   g a muscle.
I was

With Mild In.

Use commas with mild   with words like *yes* and *no*.

Well, I was almost right.
Yes, we agree to your offer.

With Direct Address

Use commas with words in direct address.

"Roberta, I need your help."

Use commas with expressions like *he said* or *plied* when used with quoted matter.

"I cannot find my raincoat," *he complained*.

With Absolute Phrases

Set off an **absolute phrase** with a comma. An absolute phrase, which consists of a noun followed by a modifier, modifies an entire sentence.

The restaurant being closed, we decided to go home.

To Prevent Misreading or to Mark an Omission

Use commas to prevent misreading or to mark an omission.

Above, the wind howled through the trees.

The summer days were hot and dry; the night, warm and humid. (comma for omitted verb *was*)

UNNECESSARY COMMAS

Between Subject and Verb

Do not use a comma between subject and verb, between verb or verbal and complement, or between an adjective and the word it modifies.

NOT
The team with the best record, will go to the playoffs.

We saw, that the window had been left open.

The shining wrapping, paper got one's attention.

Between Compound Elements

Do not use a comma between compound elements, such as verbs, subjects, complements, and predicates.

NOT
We went to the local library, and perused *The New York Times*. (compound verb; comma unnecessary)

Between Dependent Clauses

Do not use a comma before a coordinating conjunction joining two dependent clauses.

NOT
We checked to see that the lights were off, and that all the doors were locked. (comma unnecessary)

In Comparisons

Do not use a comma before *than* in a comparison or between compound conjunctions such as *as . . . as, so . . . so, so . . . that*.

The electrician found more wrong with the washing machine, than we had expected.

It was so hot, that the engine overheated.

After *Like, Such As*

Do not use a comma after *like* or *such as*.

NOT
Many famous paintings such as the *Mona Lisa* and *View of Toledo* are almost priceless.

A comma is used before *such as* only when the phrase is nonrestrictive.

Do not use a comma directly before or after a period, a question mark, an exclamation point, or a dash.

NOT
"Were you late for work?", he asked:

With Parentheses

A comma may follow a closing parenthesis but may not come before an opening parenthesis.

After reading *The Color Purple* (written by Alice Walker), one better understands the cultural roots of black Americans.

Other Unnecessary Commas

Do not use commas after coordinating conjunctions.

NOT
We did not like the accommodations at the hotel, but, we found nothing else available. (Retain comma before *but;* delete comma after *but.*)

A comma is not required after short adverbial modifiers.

After a rain the desert blooms with wildflowers. (no comma required after *rain*)

Do not use commas to set off restrictive clauses, phrases, or appositives.

NOT
The water level, *at the lake,* is low. (restrictive prepositional phrase)

Do not use a comma between adjectives that are cumulative and not coordinate. (See p. 148)

FAULTY
The new, Persian rug was beautiful.

10.1 The Comma with Independent Clauses

■ *In the following sentences, insert and encircle commas between independent clauses. In the blank at the right, enter the comma and the coordinating conjunction. If a sentence is correct, write* C.

EXAMPLE

The wheel of fortune was a significant symbol in many ancient cultures and it appears in the works of both Dante and Chaucer.   *, and*

1. About one-third of the passengers on the *Mayflower* left England for religious reasons and the other two-thirds were adventurers.   _____

2. The nuclear power industry claims that atomic plants have been criticized unfairly but many scientists believe that the problems are even greater than originally thought.   _____

3. Two word processor programs may have the same features but differ in execution.   _____

4. The Labrador retriever sat in the back of the pickup truck and it seemed to enjoy the wind blowing in its face.   _____

5. The attendants moved the animals from their small cages and relocated them in surroundings that approximated their natural habitats.   _____

6. The value of an entire coin collection mainly depends on the worth of a few rare pieces and on the condition of all the coins in a set.   _____

7. Hundreds of people crowded around the exhibit, and they appeared to enjoy the ones that provided live entertainment. _____

8. The company's comptroller personally approved all vouchers for travel expenses and warned all employees against overspending. _____

9. The diver realized the danger in attempting a new record height in the brisk wind but he asked the judges for permission to raise the platform. _____

10. Many restaurants in New England are famous for their seafood and some also have fine views of the Atlantic Ocean and the fishing boats that sail along the coast. _____

10.2 The Comma with Independent Clauses

■ *In the following sentences, insert and encircle commas between independent clauses. In the blank at the right, enter the comma and the coordinating conjunction. If a sentence is correct, write* **C**.

EXAMPLES

The farmer purchased two new tractors,and he also needed new implements.

,and

The use of alcohol as automotive fuel is hardly a new idea,for Henry Ford designed the Model T to use it.

,for

1. There were no rooms available at the resort and we had to return home.

_____

2. Vacationing in Hawaii is exciting but traveling closer to home is less expensive.

_____

3. Many students seek part-time employment during their vacations so unemployment rates rise during the summer months.

_____

4. Patience, persistence, and determination are necessary to train a dog but the most important requirement is consistency.

_____

5. Many of the books in the library were very old and the librarian knew there was little money available to save them.

_____

6. The docks were empty when the ship began to approach but suddenly they came alive with workers ready to unload the cargo.

_____

7. The small painting being auctioned was by a relatively minor sixteenth-century artist but it was valued at almost a quarter of a million dollars. _____

8. The city's Parks and Recreation Department has started evening crafts classes for adults, and these classes are attracting many people. _____

9. Dr. Cagnilia kicked her golf ball out of the sand trap, but her playing partner caught her. _____

10. Infrared photographs of the earth's geography help scientists to determine the extent of droughts and they also are invaluable aids in the search for mineral deposits. _____

10.3 The Comma with Items in a Series

■ *Insert and encircle commas as necessary in items in a series.*

EXAMPLE
The new computer is versatile portable and inexpensive.

1. Fuel oil natural gas and electricity are the most widely used sources of home energy.

2. American English continually drops old words adds new ones and develops new connotations for familiar expressions.

3. The strobe lights flashed the stereo played loudly and the revelers celebrated until morning.

4. Many recreational vehicles have complete kitchens that include compact refrigerators ranges and sinks.

5. The participants in the decathlon had completed all the events but the javelin throw the broad jump and the mile run.

6. Many families purchase garden tractors for mowing hauling and cultivating.

7. "We've itemized deductions computed our refund and signed our tax returns," sighed the weary husband.

8. We gave our dog away because in one day it had bitten the mail carrier run our neighbor's cat up a tree and chased a delivery truck.

9. Birds eat harmful insects scatter seeds and spread pollen; thus they serve a variety of ecological functions.

10. When my grandfather was young, he went to the movies on Saturday morning and watched several cartoons a serial and two movies for a mere quarter.

10.4 The Comma with Coordinate Adjectives

■ *Insert and circle commas as necessary between coordinate adjectives.*

EXAMPLE
The garden court is a new⊙exciting concept in motel design.

1. The small group was engaged in a quiet desultory conversation.

2. The bright cheerful greeting made me feel welcome.

3. Alfredo responded with quick intelligent answers when asked about his native Spain.

4. The clerk gave the customer a short rude reply.

5. The carpenter worked long hard hours on the new addition.

6. The traffic study showed that many automobiles were using the new well-designed by-pass.

7. Many people now enjoy sturdy inexpensive trampolines in their yards.

8. The student of interior design must learn the modern energy-efficient ways of accent lighting.

9. With agile deft movements, the artist sketched the scene.

10. "Laughter, I believe, is the best least expensive medicine," said the speaker.

10.5 The Comma After Introductory Clauses or Phrases

■ *Place and circle commas as needed after introductory clauses or phrases. In the space at the right, place the comma and write the word after it. If a sentence is punctuated correctly or requires no punctuation, write* **C.**

EXAMPLE
Because the administration wanted to stimulate the economy, it recommended a tax rebate.   _____, it_____

1. People who enjoy horseback riding often want
   to buy a horse.   _____

2. Although Michael liked playing in the orchestra
   he did not like practicing.   _____

3. Whatever the problem might be Jerry was usually responsible for it.   _____

4. Because the storm had torn down the power
   lines the family had to spend the night in a
   motel.   _____

5. After Linda's engagement ring had been sized
   she showed it to her friends.   _____

6. How a frustrated candidate controls himself
   and his ardent followers in defeat may determine his chances for another political race in
   the future.   _____

7. Although I was a good football player my
   brother was better than I.   _____

8. For lunch many workers drink coffee, eat a package of cheese crackers, and then return to work. _____

9. Although citizens-band radios are not as powerful as short-wave sets they nevertheless furnish hours of enjoyment to many motorists. _____

10. "Whatever we do this Saturday," Victor said, "I want to be home in time for the wrestling program on television." _____

10.6 The Comma After Introductory Clauses or Phrases

■ *Place and circle commas as needed after introductory clauses or phrases. In the space provided at the right, place the comma and write the word after it. If a sentence is punctuated correctly or requires no punctuation, write **C**.*

EXAMPLE
Although most engineers are college graduates⊙they may
need continual technical training.   *, they*

1. After the demise of vaudeville many of its stars
   became radio and television entertainers.   _____

2. Although we were separated by hundreds of
   miles, we remained friends and wrote often.   _____

3. Even though the meeting was considered a success many in the group felt much of the work
   remained unfinished.   _____

4. On Leigh's final day of classes she started pack-
   ing her clothes.   _____

5. Stepping into her limousine the diplomat suddenly turned and waved to the crowd.   _____

6. After examining their road maps travelers still
   may fail to turn onto the right road.   _____

7. Because doctors, parents, and students are re-
   questing it physical hygiene is being taught in
   many public schools.   _____

8. Although most of Mars' visible water now appears as polar ice and atmospheric vapor water may have flowed in rivers on the Martian surface thousands of years ago.   _____

9. To escape the crowd some people leave a few minutes before shops close.   _____

10. Until my ship actually sailed for the Far East, I never imagined that I would ever have the opportunity to see Japan.   _____

10.7 The Comma with Nonrestrictive Elements

■ *Correctly punctuate nonrestrictive elements in the following sentences. Write C to the right of any correctly punctuated sentence. Circle punctuation that you add.*

EXAMPLE

Emotions, which may override reason, at times cause one
to reach hasty conclusions.   _____

1. The man talking to the bank manager is my
   father.   _____

2. Pier fishing which is especially popular in this
   area, shall remain unregulated.   _____

3. The ornate weather vanes that once topped
   most American homes are again becoming
   popular.   _____

4. The letter that I wrote today should be in Portland by Thursday.   _____

5. Dr. Pamela M. Smith who is the Vice President
   for Continuing Education delivered the com-
   mencement address.   _____

6. The oak tree that is outside my bedroom window is almost as tall as our two-story house.   _____

7. Blueberries which may be cultivated in large or-
   chards make splendid jellies and jams.   _____

8. The new municipal airport which opened last
   week is several miles from the city.   _____

9. Professional counseling in elementary school which is a relatively new field can make a dramatic difference in the scholastic performance of young children. _____

10. John Richardson who is the chef at my father's restaurant does not like to prepare food for large groups. _____

10.8   The Comma—All Uses

■ *Correctly punctuate the following sentences. Circle punctuation that you add.*

EXAMPLE

Denver, Colorado, and San Diego, California, are two of the most rapidly growing cities in the United States.

1. On July 1 1985 we will begin a new training program for our older employees.

2. Alicia McMurray C.P.A. was employed by the firm of Feldman Parsons and Ames.

3. We wrote a letter to our congressman's regional office in Richmond Virginia to complain about his recent stand on taxes.

4. "In conclusion" said the long-winded dull speaker "I would like to thank all of you for coming—men women boys girls—all of you."

5. The international Morse code a form of the original Morse code used in international telegraphy is sometimes called the continental code.

6. Whenever we hear that snow has fallen in the nearby mountains we pack up the car and spend the weekend there.

7. The American Council of Learned Societies located at 345 East 46th Street New York New York 10017 sponsors many kinds of fellowships in various academic disciplines.

8. On this date October 12 1984 the small collection of houses called Arno New Mexico was formally incorporated and it installed its first mayor city council and school board.

9. "Although it is a relatively small city Bismarck North Dakota is the state capital and is twice as large as Pierre South Dakota which is also a state capital" stated the visiting lecturer in Geography 101.

10. Sandra O'Connor a jurist from Arizona is the first woman appointed to the United States Supreme Court.

10.9 The Comma—All Uses

■ *Correctly punctuate the following sentences. Circle punctuation that you add. Write*
C in the blank at the right if the sentence is correct.

EXAMPLE
The good speaker, using an occasional pause, allows an
audience a chance to respond.   _____

1. The woman in charge of personnel Margaret
   Childes requires a psychological profile of each
   new employee.   _____

2. Any citizen of the United States may communi-
   cate with the President simply by addressing a
   letter to 1600 Pennsylvania Avenue Washington
   DC 20500.   _____

3. Although pumice is quite porous and even appears to be spongy it is a form of volcanic rock
   used as an abrasive.   _____

4. "The Book Exchange" the notice read "will be
   open on Monday December 19."   _____

5. To settle legal disputes among themselves
   many nations turn to the International Court of
   Justice the main judicial body of the United Nations.   _____

6. We finally could not resist playing a practical
   joke on Raymond because he had played so
   many on us.   _____

7. The eager industrious volunteers worked to complete the homecoming float.

_____

8. Lifting the antique glass to the light to examine its color, examining the engraving and lightly tapping its sides the expert judged it to be quite valuable.

_____

9. To a shaggy long-haired dog that can find little relief from the summer heat a cool bare concrete floor is a great blessing.

_____

10. On January 18 1986 Charles Richardson an active man throughout his life will celebrate his eighty-seventh birthday.

_____

10.10 Unnecessary Commas

■ *Circle all unnecessary commas in the following sentences.*

EXAMPLE

A citizen₍,₎ who never votes₍,₎ should not criticize elected officials.

1. The mountains near our home are noted for the beautiful, clear lakes, and the many, types of birds and plants.

2. The ferocious, black hornet is really a member of the wasp family, and, is, believe it or not, a very social insect.

3. The dingo, a wolf-like, wild, dog of Australia, is a natural enemy of sheep herds.

4. In *The Red Badge of Courage*, Stephen Crane brings to life, the psychological conflicts of young Henry Fleming, the hero.

5. An unusually large, black, bat quickly flew from room to room in the caverns, several hundred feet underground.

6. Of some botanical interest, is a plant called, rattlesnake root, which has tubers that supposedly cure rattlesnake bites—, at least many early settlers thought so.

7. The famous, Oregon Trail covered two thousand miles of frontier from Independence, Missouri, to Portland, Oregon, and was heavily traveled, during the westward migrations of the nineteenth century.

8. The unusually, careful driver ahead of us slowed everyone in our lane.

9. One of the shells, that we found at the beach turned out to be valuable.

10. The last of the South American artifacts, shown at the museum, were packed, and prepared for shipping at the end of the week.

10.11 Unnecessary Commas

■ *Circle all unnecessary commas in the following sentences.*

EXAMPLE

Edward and Nancy⊙graduated earlier than expected.

1. "A gentleman, sir," he quoted, "kneels only to pray, or propose. Furthermore, a gentleman removes his tie, only for sleeping."

2. When invited to an informal cookout, she appears, in fashionable, attire of fiery, red, and orange, silk; and her husband, always, wears a baggy, wrinkled, brown suit.

3. Of all the poems I have read recently, Thomas Hardy's lyric, "The Darkling Thrush," and Alfred, Lord Tennyson's, *In Memoriam*, seem the most pertinent to our times.

4. The shadow of the massive, ageless, oak fell upon the young, and carefree lovers, as they planned with infinite faith, for the future.

5. So great was the influence of Thomas Paine, on his own time, that John Adams suggested, that the era be called, "The Age of Paine."

6. One should never be ashamed, however, of being somewhat sentimental, for, a certain amount of sentimentality, can help keep a person warm and human.

7. By 1910, some demographers predicted, that the population of Western Europe would begin to decline, and that, by the end of the century, Eastern Europe would be more populous than Western Europe.

8. Efficient, construction workers at the building site completed the foundation in less than a week.

9. Our new piano will be delivered this week, possibly, by Wednesday.

10. The Coast Guard launch, skipped across the water, quickly slowed, and then turned, toward the pier.

Semicolon, Colon, Dash, Parentheses, Brackets

THE SEMICOLON

Between Two Independent Clauses

Use a semicolon between independent clauses not joined by *and, but, or, nor, for, so,* or *yet.*

We hiked to the top of the mountain; we looked out over a valley covered with wildflowers.

Use a semicolon with a conjunctive adverb when it is followed by an independent clause.

We stayed until late afternoon; then we made our way back to camp.

Use a semicolon to separate independent clauses that are long and complex or that have internal punctuation.

Central City, located near Denver, was once a mining town; but now it is noted for its summer opera program.

Between Items in a Series

Use semicolons in a series between items that have internal punctuation (usually commas).

In his closet Bill kept a photograph album, which was empty; several tennis shoes, all with holes in them; and the radiator cap from his first car, which he sold his first year in college.

Do not use a semicolon between elements that are not coordinate.

INCORRECT
After publishing *The Day of the Jackal* and several other popular novels; Frederick Forsyth wrote his most exciting book, *The Devil's Alternative.* (Use a comma, not a semicolon.)

THE COLON

Use the colon before quotations, statements, and series that are introduced formally.

The geologist began his speech with a disturbing statement: "This country is short of rare metals."

Use a colon to introduce a formal series.

Bring the following items: food for a week, warm clothes, bedding, and a canteen.

Between Two Independent Clauses

Use a colon between two independent clauses when the second explains the first.

The team's record was excellent: we have not lost a game this season.

For Special Uses

Use the colon between hours and minutes.

4:35 P.M.

Unnecessary Colon

Do not use a colon *after* a linking verb or a preposition.

INCORRECT
Our representatives are: Anne Crane and Andrew Miles.
He was accustomed to: hard work, good pay, and long weekends.

THE DASH

Use the dash to introduce summaries or to show interruption, parenthetical comment, or special emphasis.

For Summary

Clothing, blankets, food, medicine—anything will help.

For Interruption

"I want to say how sad—I mean happy—I am to be here," the speaker stumbled.

For Parenthetical Comments

This is important—I mean really important—so listen carefully.

For Special Emphasis

The key to the mystery could only be in one place—the attic.

176

PARENTHESES

Use parentheses to enclose loosely related comments or explanations or to enclose numbers used to indicate items in a series.

That year (1950) was the happiest time of my life.

Please do the following: (1) fill out the form, (2) include a check or money order, and (3) list any special mailing instructions.

BRACKETS

Use brackets to enclose *interpolations,* that is, the writer's explanations, within a passage that is being quoted.

The senator objected, "I cannot agree with your [Senator Miner's] reasoning." (brackets used to set off writer's interpolation)

11.3 Colons and Dashes

■ *Correctly punctuate the following sentences. Circle punctuation that you add. Write C to the left of any sentence that is correct.*

EXAMPLE

All of New England—Connecticut, Maine, Massachusetts, New Hampshire, Rhode Island, and Vermont—is likely to suffer serious fuel shortages during bad winters.

1. The quarterback's play a tight-end screen pass surprised both the defense and the fans.

2. Many theaters find that an 815 curtain time means fewer latecomers than one at 800.

3. The cotton gin invented by a man from Massachusetts on a visit to Georgia helped to shape the economic destinies of both North and South.

4. A good bird watcher makes identifications using the following characteristics voice, color, size, type of bill, markings, and range.

5. There is only one quality that endears two-year-olds to those around them their desire to imitate adults.

6. Ragweed, mesquite, pine all produce common allergies.

7. The most common means of evaluation the intelligence test is no longer considered sufficient as the sole criterion for placement in special classes.

8. All of us John, Mary, and I wanted the opening on the debate team.

9. After the FAA completed its examination of the wreckage, it concluded that there could be only one reason for the crash pilot error.

10. Halfway down the page the following admonition appeared in bold print DO NOT WRITE BELOW THIS LINE.

11.4 Parentheses and Brackets

■ *Insert parentheses and brackets where they are needed in the following sentences. Circle parentheses and brackets that you add.*

EXAMPLE

Some energy problems (choosing hazardous waste sites, for example) are also political.

1. The administration of Franklin D. Roosevelt 1932–1945 was the longest of any President's.

2. Saint Valentine's Day February 14 is observed in honor of a Christian martyr.

3. Boise which rhymes with "noisy" is the capital of Idaho; it was built on the Oregon Trail.

4. The agronomist considered soybeans as the crop of the future because 1 they have few natural enemies; 2 they are high in protein; and 3 they require relatively little expensive fertilizer.

5. Seventeen thousand new Flashback cars the model had just been introduced had to be recalled because of faulty brakes.

6. The expert on etiquette she had written four books on the subject concluded: "Good manners reveal it good breeding; therefore, one should take it seriously."

7. Many physicians believe that most people would enjoy good health if they would a eat modestly, b exercise regularly, and c maintain an optimistic attitude.

8. Before going on a vacation, people should 1 stop all deliveries, 2 ask a neighbor to watch their house, and 3 make certain that all doors are locked and all windows are securely closed.

9. Someone we think it is Mike Erlich has been circulating memos that are quite funny to the office staff.

10. "That was the year 1965," he said, "that we planned to expand our market to include the West Coast."

12

Quotation Marks and End Punctuation

QUOTATION MARKS

Use quotation marks to enclose the exact words of a speaker or writer.

"I'm tired," he said. (declarative statement and object of verb *said*)

"Come here," she demanded. (command)

"Who's ready to leave?" Mary asked. (question)

"Quick!" he shouted. (exclamation)

Periods and *commas* always are placed inside quotation marks. *Semicolons* and *colons* always are placed outside quotation marks. *Question marks* and *exclamation points* are placed inside quotation marks when they refer to the quotation itself. They are placed outside the quotation marks when they refer to the entire sentence.

Who said, "We need a new car"? (Quotation is a statement.)

Use quotation marks to enclose dialogue. Do not use quotation marks with indirect quotation.

Alexander Pope once wrote, "A little learning is a dangerous thing." (direct quotation)

Alexander Pope said that a little learning can be dangerous. (indirect quotation)

In dialogue a new paragraph marks each change of speaker.

"Do you have change for a dollar?" the customer asked, after searching in his pocket for change.
"I think so," replied the cashier.

Quotation Within a Quotation

Use single quotation marks to enclose a quotation within a quotation.

John complained, "I don't understand your comment, 'Be clear first, then clever.'"

Titles

Use quotation marks to enclose the titles of essays, articles, short stories, chapters, television programs that are not serials, and short musical compositions.

We enjoy reading William Safire's column, "On Language," in the Sunday newspaper. (article in newspaper)

The band began to play Sousa's "Stars and Stripes Forever." (musical composition)

Unnecessary Quotations

Do not use quotation marks to emphasize or change the usual meanings of words or to point out the use of slang or attempts at humor. If you must use such language, let it stand without comment.

NOT

We had a "great" time at the party. (emphasis)

That movie was really "bad." (change of meaning)

I guess we "goofed." (slang)

His lemonades are so bad that they always turn out to be "lemons." (attempted humor)

ND PUNCTUATION

eriod after sentences that make statements and after sentences command which is not exclamatory.

us uncomfortable. (statement)

Meet u. t. (mild command)

Use a que after a direct question.

What time is it?

Use an exclamation p fter a word, a phrase, or a sentence to indicate strong feeling.

Ouch! That hurt!

Stop that man!

Remember to use a period afte xclamations.

That is the craziest idea I ever heard.

12.1 Quotation Marks and End Punctuation

■ *Correctly punctuate the following sentences. Circle any incorrect punctuation and indicate what punctuation should be used. Indicate a new paragraph with the sign ¶.*

EXAMPLE

"What kind of trees are those?" asked the tourist. ¶ "Redwoods," replied the ranger.

1. My ring is gone cried the frantic woman.

2. "Well!" the sergeant said, you don't have my permission."

3. Keep your bike in top condition for safe riding said the instruction booklet.

4. What sort of experience leads a young person to choose the life of a surgeon inquired the patient.

5. The social scientist summarized as follows: Because young people generally have values in opposition to those of adult society, youth can be classified as a genuine subculture.

6. An increase in radon in well water said the science reporter may become a means for geologists to predict earthquakes.

7. So many foreign visitors were anticipated by Greek officials that they made arrangements for several ships to provide accommodations for tourists without hotel reservations explained the travel agent.

8. Stop You've tried my patience to the limit

9. The press corps asked exactly what the role of the President's science adviser would be?

10. Did you know that some of the officers in   n Revolu-

    tion came to this country from Poland sp   help us win

    the war asked the history instructor. Ou   laski, Tennes-

    see, is named for one of them a stud   ed. Correct that

    was Count Pulaski responded the te

12.2 Quotation Marks and End Punctuation

■ *Correctly punctuate the following sentences. Circle any incorrect punctuation. Indicate a new paragraph with the sign ¶.*

EXAMPLE
The referee's cry (Stop! You're out of bounds) was lost in the noise of the crowd.

1. The article discussed why boys and girls differ in behavior even before puberty?

2. To freeze peaches droned the television chef use citric acid to prevent the fruit from turning brown.

3. Although "considered strange" by his friends, Raymond was actually only very shy.

4. "Why do I have to go to the dentist," the child asked?

5. "Who said, "The only place he'd be the life of the party is in a mortuary?"

6. Quick the driver screamed to the passerby the light will change shortly.

7. When my daughter completes her B.S. continued the proud father she expects to begin work toward her M.S. and eventually to earn her Ph.D.

8. When the diner looked at the burned steak, he complained to the waiter, "I said well-done, not cremated". You said very well-done, sir replied the waiter.

9. "None of the current methods of increasing the energy supply of American appears to be adequate", writes Wilson Clark in "It takes Energy to Get Energy".

10. Can you come by the house today? Mary asked. No, I haven't the time, Craig answered. But I can come tomorrow. Fine, I'll see you then.

Mechanics

Italics

Italicize (underline) titles of independent publications (books, magazines, newspapers) and, occasionally, words to be emphasized.

Underline titles of books (except the Bible and its divisions), periodicals, newspapers, motion pictures, long musical compositions (operas and symphonies, for example), works of art, plays, and other works published separately.

TITLES

Books
The World Almanac

Periodicals
Psychology Today

Newspapers
Washington Post or the Washington Post

Motion Pictures
Star Wars

Musical Compositions, Paintings, and Sculpture
Handel's Messiah

Rodin's The Thinker

Plays
The Tempest

NAMES OF SHIPS AND TRAINS

Underline the names of ships and trains.

The U.S.S. Nimitz

the Zephyr

FOREIGN WORDS

Underline foreign words used in an English context if they have not become a part of our language. Check the dictionary before underlining foreign words.

194

The nachalstvo, the privileged class of Russian Communist Party members, are afforded the same luxuries available to the wealthy in any other country.

WORDS BEING NAMED

Underline words, letters, and figures being named.

The word credenza, which now refers to a table, once was associated with poison.
Your m's look like n's.

FOR OCCASIONAL EMPHASIS

Although underlining for emphasis is permissible on occasion, avoid excessive underlining because it often reveals a writer's weak vocabulary.

NOT
That's not just a big dinner. That's a big dinner.

IMPROVED
That's not just a big dinner. That's a feast.

13.1 Italics

■ *Underline for italics in the following sentences.*

EXAMPLE
<u>The Verdict</u> is a superb movie about modern journalism.

1. Unlike other newspapers, USA Today is distributed nationwide.

2. Lorry is the British word for truck.

3. People learning to pronounce English as a foreign language often find l's, g's, and k's to be troublesome.

4. The launching of the space shuttle Columbia was watched by millions of Americans.

5. Millions of tourists see Charles Lindbergh's aircraft, the Spirit of St. Louis, at the Smithsonian Institution.

6. The British film Chariots of Fire won an Academy Award.

7. The United States Navy recommissioned the U.S.S. New Jersey, a World War II battleship.

8. William Least Heat Moon's journal Blue Highways appeared in 1982.

9. Peter and the Wolf is a musical composition written especially for children.

10. The decision was a fait accompli before any discussion concerning its implications.

13.2 Italics

■ *Underline for italics in the following sentences.*

EXAMPLE
Audubon: A Vision is a long poem by Robert Penn Warren.

1. The United States, not the Queen Elizabeth II, was the largest ocean liner ever built.

2. Roger Tory Peterson's A Field Guide to the Birds has been called the authorative book for bird watchers.

3. A recent article in Science Digest discusses the relatively new field of sports medicine.

4. The word urbane has been used to describe magazines such as National Geographic and Discover.

5. Agatha Christie's The Mousetrap holds the record as the longest running play.

6. A roman à clef is a novel like Thomas Wolfe's Look Homeward, Angel, which presents real people and events under fictional guises.

7. Ordinary People was not only a popular novel but also an Academy Award winning film.

8. Vivaldi's Four Seasons is a masterpiece of baroque music.

9. The Empire Strikes Back is a sequel to Star Wars.

10. The Washington Post is the only newspaper published in Washington, D.C.

Spelling

Spell correctly. Use the dictionary when you are uncertain of the spelling of a word.

Be particularly careful of words that are not spelled as they sound (*though* and *debt*), words that sound the same (*sew* and *so*), words with the "uh" sound, which gives no clue to their spelling (*terrible* and *persistent*).

Do not misspell words by omitting a syllable that is occasionally not pronounced (*accidently* for *accidentally*), by adding syllables (*mischievious* for *mischievous*), or by changing syllables (*preform* for *perform*).

GUIDES FOR SPELLING

For *ie* and *ei*

Use *i* before *e* (*believe*) except after *c* (*receive*) or when these letters are sounded as *a* (*neighbor*). There are a few exceptions (*either, neither, leisure, seize, weird, height*).

Final *e*

Drop the final *e* when adding a **suffix** if the suffix begins with a vowel (*dine* to *dining*). Keep the *e* if the suffix begins with a consonant (*improve* to *improvement*). There are some exceptions (for example, *judge* becomes *judgment, notice* becomes *noticeable,* and *awe* becomes *awful*).

For Changing *y* to *i*

Change the *y* to *i* when the *y* is preceded by a consonant, but not when the *y* is preceded by a vowel or when *-ing* is added (*story* becomes *stories, delay* becomes *delays,* and *fly* becomes *flying*).

Suffixes

If the suffix begins with a consonant, do not double the final consonant of a word (*quick* becomes *quickly*). If the suffix begins with a vowel, double the last consonant of one-syllable words (*bat* becomes *batting*) and of words of more than one syllable if the accent is on the last syllable (*occur'* becomes *occurrence*). Do not double the final consonant if that consonant is preceded by two vowels (*repair* becomes *repairing*), or if the word ends with two or more consonants (*drink* becomes *drinking)*, or if the last syllable of the word is not stressed after the suffix is added *(prefer'* becomes *pref'erence)*.

Plurals

Add *-s* for plurals of most nouns *(sound* becomes *sounds)* and for nouns ending in *o* when it is preceded by a vowel *(portfolio* becomes *portfolios)*. Add *-es* when the plural has another syllable that is pronounced *(speech* becomes *speeches)* and in most cases when the noun ends in *o* preceded by a consonant *(tomato* becomes *tomatoes)*. See a dictionary for the exceptions.

The plurals of proper names are generally formed by adding *-s* or *-es (Taylor, Taylors; Jones, Joneses)*.

HYPHENATION AND SYLLABICATION

Use a hyphen in certain compound words and in words divided at the end of a line.

It is best to consult a dictionary to determine whether a compound word is hyphenated or is written as one or two words. Hyphenate a compound of two or more words used as a single modifier before a noun.

HYPHEN
He is a *well-known* millionaire.

NO HYPHEN
The millionaire is *well known*.

Hyphenate spelled-out compound numbers from *twenty-one* through *ninety-nine*.

When hyphenating a word at the end of a line, do not divide one-syllable words, do not put a one-letter syllable on a separate line *(a-long,* for example) and avoid carrying over a two-letter suffix to another line *(pock-et)*. Divide words according to the syllabication in the dictionary.

202

14.1 Suffixes

■ *In the blank spaces provided, write the correct spellings of the following words.*

EXAMPLE

cite / ing ___*citing*_____

1. compel / ing _____

2. devastate / ing _____

3. note / able _____

4. notice / able _____

5. real / ity _____

6. forbid / en _____

7. write / ing _____

8. symptom / atic _____

9. eat / able _____

10. real / istic _____

11. full / ness _____

12. like / able _____

13. subdue / ing _____

14. interchange / able _____

15. mass / ive _____

16. beauty / eous _____

17. commit / ing _____

18. reverse / ible _____

19. begin / ing _____

20. occur / ing _____

21. fry / ed _____

22. fry / ing _____

23. plural / istic _____

24. recur / ed _____

25. cancel / ed _____

14.2 Suffixes

■ *In the blank spaces provided, write the correct spellings of the following words.*

EXAMPLE

stop / ing _____*stopping*_____

1. denote / ation _____

2. believe / able _____

3. tardy / ness _____

4. possible / ity _____

5. compassion / ate _____

6. invalid / ate _____

7. true / ly _____

8. lone / liness _____

9. conceive / able _____

10. envy / able _____

11. net / ing _____

12. direct / ory _____

13. endure / ed _____

14. prescribe / ing _____

15. admit / ance _____

16. marvel / ous _____

17. travel / ed _____

18. adequate / ly _____

19. courage / ous _____

20. explore / ation _____

21. judge / ment _____

22. achieve / ment _____

23. pretty / ly _____

24. guarantee / ing _____

25. propose / al _____

14.3 Spelling with *ie* and *ei*

■ *Fill in the blanks in the following words with* **ie** *or* **ei**.

EXAMPLE

defic__*ie*__nt

1. consc_____nce

2. rel_____ve

3. conc_____t

4. m_____n

5. d_____gn

6. p_____r

7. financ_____r

8. s_____ve

9. dec_____t

10. _____ther

11. ser_____s

12. rel_____ve

13. v_____w

14. fr_____nd

15. n_____ce

16. for_____gn

17. f_____gn

18. conc_____ve

19. s_____ge

20. n_____ther

21. sc_____nce

22. rec_____pt

23. dec_____ve

24. h_____ght

25. s_____ze

NAME _____

DATE _____ SCORE _____

14.4 Spelling with *ie* and *ei*

■ *Fill in the blanks in the following words with **ie** or **ei**.*

EXAMPLE

prem_ie_r

1. forf_____t

2. f_____ld

3. retr_____ve

4. p_____ce

5. shr_____k

6. y_____ld

7. ach_____ve

8. d_____gn

9. fr_____ght

10. h_____r

11. pr_____st

12. consc_____ntious

13. n_____ghbor

14. r_____gn

15. sl_____gh

16. omnisc_____nt

17. n_____gh

18. bel_____ve

19. perc_____ve

20. w_____ght

21. l_____sure

22. c_____ling

23. mil_____u

24. pl_____rs

25. G_____ger counter

14.5 Plurals

■ *Form the plural for each of the following nouns. If there is more than one plural form, give all of them. Consult your dictionary when in doubt.*

EXAMPLE

bush _____*bushes*_____

1. elf _____

2. courtesy _____

3. trepidation _____

4. bastion _____

5. bureaucracy _____

6. cargo _____

7. gypsy _____

8. thief _____

9. antenna _____

10. oasis _____

11. antithesis _____

12. bookshelf _____

13. hero _____

14. committee _____

15. trauma _____

16. village _____

17. essay _____

18. cemetery _____

19. embargo _____

20. locust _____

21. halo _____

22. alumnus _____

23. manifesto _____

24. medium _____

25. criterion _____

14.6 Hyphenation

■ *Write the correct spelling of the following compounds in the blanks at the right. If a spelling is correct, write C in the blank. Consult a recent dictionary.*

EXAMPLES

hat-less _____ *hatless* _____

reenter _____ *re-enter* _____

1. road-side _____

2. now-a-days _____

3. sea-side _____

4. eighty five _____

5. letter-head _____

6. de escalate _____

7. one-hundred _____

8. trans continental _____

9. nation wide _____

10. laissez faire _____

11. baby sitter _____

12. one-twelfth _____

13. half truth _____

14. per centage _____

15. per cent _____

16. non fiction _____

17. thing in itself _____

18. hub bub _____

19. semi solid _____

20. great grandmother _____

21. pro American _____

22. all-purpose _____

23. re-write _____

24. excouncilman _____

25. sub-terranean _____

NAME _____

DATE _____ SCORE _____

14.7 Hyphenation and Syllabication

■ *Circle errors in hyphenation or syllabication and correct them. Add hyphens where necessary.*

EXAMPLE
The○nce-popular convertible is again on the market.

1. The cashier short-changed the customer.

2. The garden-club committee will meet at ten on Thursday morning.

3. A trouble shooter came from the Maintenance Department.

4. We had a long and involved discussion in class today over the u-sage of a word in our textbook.

5. When I met Susan, I knew she was a-born leader.

6. Physicians warn that quack remedies for arthritis—apple-cider, vinegar, a dry-climate, or a copper-bracelet—have no medical value.

7. Bills de-signed to ex-pand the active work force have been introduced in the House-of-Representatives.

8. Some political theorists believe that the Attorney-General should be independent of the White-House, and a congressional subcommittee is studying this suggestion.

9. The Department of Public Safety tries to discourage hitch hikers because many of them are victimized by so called Good Samaritan drivers.

10. An increase of white collar jobs, a decrease of blue collar jobs, and an increase in the number of working wives will mean that 30 per cent of all American families will earn $25,000 or more by 1990.

Apostrophes, Capitals, and Numbers

APOSTROPHES

Use the apostrophe for the possessive case of many nouns, contractions, omissions, and some plurals.

Use 's for the possessive of nouns not ending in s.

SINGULAR	PLURAL
child's, worker's	people's, women's

Use 's or ' without the s for possessive of singular nouns ending in s. Do not add the s when a singular noun ending in s is followed by a word that begins with s.

Dennis's, or Dennis' *but not* Dennis's stories

Use ' without the s to form the possessive of plural nouns ending in s.

the Howards' vacation, the actresses' dressing room

Use 's to form the possessive of indefinite pronouns.

anyone's, everybody's, neither's

Use 's with only the last noun when indicating joint possession in a pair or series.

Elizabeth and Bob's car was new. (They own the car together.)
Elizabeth's and Bob's cars were new. (They each own a car.)

Use ' to show omissions or to form contractions.

the '80s, won't, it's (it is)

Use 's to form the plural of numerals, letters, and words being named.

five 9's, three b's

CAPITAL LETTERS

Use a capital letter to begin a sentence and to designate a proper noun.

Capitalize the first word in a sentence, the letter *I*, and the interjection *O*.

What, O what, have I done?

Capitalize the first, last, and important words in titles, including the second part of hyphenated words.

Great Expectations
The Man with the Golden Horn
Slaughterhouse-Five

Capitalize first words in quotations and words capitalized by the author.

"We could call this the Age of Indifference," the author wrote.

Capitalize titles preceding names.

Admiral Halsey

Capitalize titles of the leader of a nation even when the name of the person is not given. Capitalize titles that substitute for specific names.

The Prime Minister is in conference.
General Ames has been in Europe. The General has been inspecting NATO units.

A title not followed by a name is usually not capitalized.

The chairman counted the votes.

Titles which are common nouns that name an office are not capitalized.

A private has a hard life.

Capitalize degrees and titles after names.

Alice Trevor, Management Consultant
Denise Lattimore, M.D.

Capitalize words of family relationships used as names when not preceded by a possessive pronoun.

I know Dad will want to see the game.

Capitalize proper nouns and their derivatives.

Paris, Parisian; the Southwest; Democrats, the Democratic Party; the Missouri River; Middle Atlantic States

Capitalize movements, periods, and events in history.

the Victorian Period, the Spanish-American War

Capitalize words referring to the Deity, to religious denominations, and to religious literature. Pronouns referring to the Deity are usually capitalized.

God, Methodism, the Bible
We know He is our God.

Capitalize the titles of specific courses and the names of languages.

English 101, Mathematics 235
Math 101 *but not* a Math course (because not specific)

ABBREVIATIONS

Avoid most abbreviations in writing. Spell out the names of days, months, units of measurement, and (except in addresses) states and countries. In addresses use the abbreviations of the U.S. Postal Service (NY, CA, TX).

Monday (*not* Mon.); February (*not* Feb.); ounce (*not* oz.); Fort Worth, Texas (*not* TX)

Abbreviations are acceptable before names (Mr., Dr.), after names (Sr., D.D.S.), and with dates and time (B.C., A.D. and A.M., P.M.).

NUMBERS

Spell out numbers that can be written in one word.

forty-five

Use figures for other numbers.

12,367, $978.34, 3⅓

Never begin sentences with numbers. Rephrase the sentence or spell the numbers out.

NOT
50 men started work.

BUT

Fifty men started work.

OR

There were fifty men who started work.

Use numerals for figures in a series.

We bought 10 pounds of potatoes, 2 quarts of milk, and 2 dozen eggs.

Use figures for dates, street numbers, page references, percentages, and hours of the day used with A.M. or P.M.

USE FIGURES	SPELL OUT
March 7, 1981	the seventh of March
4511 Mary Ellen Avenue	Tenth Street
See page 10.	The book has twenty pages
He paid 10 percent interest	
The meeting starts at 10 P.M.	The meeting starts at ten o'clock

15.1 The Apostrophe

■ *Give the singular possessive and the plural possessive of the following nouns.*

EXAMPLE
campaign   *campaign's*   *campaigns'*

	SINGULAR POSSESSIVE	PLURAL POSSESSIVE
1. witness	_____	_____
2. wife	_____	_____
3. devotee	_____	_____
4. Rivera (last name)	_____	_____
5. slogan	_____	_____
6. Kent (last name)	_____	_____
7. genius	_____	_____
8. Perez (last name)	_____	_____
9. druggist	_____	_____
10. dictionary	_____	_____
11. heroine	_____	_____
12. cemetery	_____	_____
13. poet	_____	_____
14. girl	_____	_____
15. fox	_____	_____
16. church	_____	_____
17. Mathis (last name)	_____	_____
18. attorney	_____	_____

	SINGULAR POSSESSIVE	PLURAL POSSESSIVE
19. mother-in-law	_____	_____
20. workman	_____	_____
21. specimen	_____	_____
22. Pakistani	_____	_____
23. Westerner	_____	_____
24. library	_____	_____
25. judge	_____	_____

15.2 The Apostrophe

■ *Add apostrophes where necessary and circle incorrect apostrophes. Change spellings where appropriate.*

EXAMPLES

Almost everyones'o imagination was captivated by the success of the space shuttle. (plural possessive changed to singular possessive)

Ten library's orders were delivered late. (singular possessive changed to plural possessive)

1. Hundreds of toy's built on our main plants assembly line were returned because they were defective.

2. The physicians' prognosis' was optimistic.

3. At the waters edge we discovered a beautiful piece of driftwood.

4. Charles attitude toward his fellow workers changed when he knew them better and began to spend his evening's with them.

5. The Waitresses Guild decided to hold it's 78 convention in Chicago because of the citys' good accommodations.

6. Most of the attorneys day—from eight oclock until two oclock—is spent in hearings, committee meetings, and court sessions.

7. The groom followed his future father-in-laws advice and carefully hid his car before the wedding days festivities.

8. The calculator sputtered and erroneously registered eight 7s across the screen, and these were immediately followed by a series of Es.

9. The children said the toys were their's, not the neighbors children's.

10. The quarterbacks and the wide receivers intuitions about the defenses plays made them an extraordinarily effective offensive combination.

15.3 Capitals

■ *Correct the errors in capitalization.*

EXAMPLE
Video Cassette Recorders and Home Computers are becoming less expensive.

1. The transAmerica building in San Francisco has been compared to a heightened pyramid or an obelisk.

2. The yukon river flows in a northwesterly direction for approximately 1979 miles and empties into the bering sea.

3. People often burn a Yule log at Christmas.

4. Many critics believe that Educational Television has matured because of its excellent production of Children's Programs.

5. The climax of Shakespeare's *King Richard III* comes when king Richard says, "a horse! a horse! my kingdom for a horse!"

6. The english word *Young* comes from the swedish word for heather, *ljung;* the english obviously changed *lj* into *y.*

7. Summer Stock Companies often make up in *esprit de corps* what they lack in theatrical sophistication and experience.

8. Winston Churchill, prime minister of great Britain during the second world war, was the unlikely author of a book on Art called *Painting for Pleasure.*

9. Eric Arthur Blair, known to the Public as George Orwell, was a British Essayist who satirized modern politicians for their use of such phrases as *render inoperative, militate against, make contact with, be subjected to,* and *make itself felt.*

10. The septuagint, one of the earliest texts of the bible, is the oldest Greek version of the old testament; Legend says that it was translated by seventy jewish scholars at the request of Ptolemy II of Egypt.

15.4 Abbreviations and Numbers

■ *Correct unacceptable usage of abbreviations and numbers. Write corrections above the line.*

EXAMPLE

> *100* *first*
> We sold ~~one hundred~~ sweaters during the ~~1st~~ day of the sale.

1. We chose Apr. fifteenth as an appropriate date to hear Rep. Hastings' views on income tax.

2. 35% of our stock was sold the 1st day the store opened.

3. When we retire in 86, we plan to move to a small town just outside Denver, Colo.

4. The Metro. Transit Authority purchased 22 new buses for two million, four hundred, forty thousand dollars.

5. Occupancy rates of hotels in some resort areas climbed as high as 90% during the Bicentennial celebration.

6. One lineman weighed two hundred fifty lbs.; another, two hundred forty lbs.; the third, two hundred sixty lbs.; and the last, two hundred eighty lbs.—all for an average weight of 257 pt. 5 lbs.

7. The *New York Times* sent its best reporters to Wash., D.C., to cover the White House, Sen., and House of Rep.

8. Economists agree that countries with fifty percent inflation are in deep financial trouble.

9. On the twenty-fourth of Dec. ea. year community choirs across the U.S. go caroling.

10. Rev. Smith, Sen. Martinez, and Capt. Briggs of the A.F. were present for the commissioning of the new Lts.

Diction and Style

16

The Dictionary and Standard English

THE DICTIONARY

Dictionaries contain information that is necessary for precise writing. The following entry from the *American Heritage Dictionary* for the word *bureaucrat* indicates the kinds of information that are found in an entry. The numbers in brackets have been added.

bureaucrat [1] byoor'ə-krăt) [2] *n.* [3] 1. An official of a bureaucracy. 2. Any official who insists on rigid adherence to rules, forms, and routines. [4]— bureaucratic *adj.* bureaucratically *adv.*

[5] *Usage:* In American usage *bureaucrat* is almost invariably derogatory, unless the context establishes otherwise.

After the word is the following information: (1) the pronunciation and syllabication of the word, (2) the part of speech, (3) the definitions of the word, (4) the ways the word is spelled for other parts of speech, and (5) the way the word is used.

Dictionaries also include the following:

1. Principal parts of regular and irregular verbs, degrees of adjectives and adverbs, and irregular forms of nouns
2. Comparative and superlative degrees of adjectives and adverbs
3. Plurals of nouns
4. Archaic forms of inflected verbs (*doest* for the second-person present tense of *do*)
5. Labels for the technical or limited use of words (*chemistry* or *sports*, for example)
6. Other labels indicating restricted usage (*nonstandard, slang, poetic, foreign languages*)
7. Cross-references to other words and spelling variations
8. Etymologies
9. Synonyms
10. Standard abbreviations
11. Miscellaneous information, including references to famous people, to geographic areas, and to important historical movements and periods

USAGE

Standard English is the accepted language of English-speaking people. In formal writing, avoid using words that are not considered standard. Replace nonstandard words in most kinds of prose. Read the labels in a current dictionary.

NOT
She was fired up about her new job.

BUT
She was excited about her new job.

IMPROPRIETIES

Improprieties are the uses of words as the wrong parts of speech or the incorrect uses of words for similar words that have different meanings.

IMPROPRIETY	PROPER FORMS
ice tea (noun for adjective)	iced tea
easy understood (adjective for adverb)	easily understood
except a gift	*accept* a gift
brake a glass	*break* a glass

IDIOMS

Idioms are accepted expressions with meanings that differ from the meanings of the individual words themselves.

The actor told his co-star to go on stage and *break a leg*. (to do her best)

Many idioms are incorrect because the wrong prepositions are used.

UNIDIOMATIC	IDIOMATIC
conform with	conform to
oblivious of	oblivious to
in reference with	in reference to
the year of 1981	the year 1981

TRITENESS

Triteness includes worn-out or hackneyed phrases and figures of speech. Substitutes that are fresh and original should be used. Avoid such expressions as the following.

AVOID
if and when	out of the frying pan and into the fire
trials and tribulations	darkness before the dawn
never rains but it pours	putting salt on a wound

CORRECTNESS

Correct usage requires a knowledge of idioms, the use of a current dictionary, and wide experience with words. Words must be used precisely; writers must avoid using words that are confusing and vague.

The *astrologer* scientifically studied the moons of Jupiter. (The word should be *astronomer*.)

He was in difficult *straights*. (The word should be *straits*, meaning a difficult situation.)

WORDINESS

Wordiness is the use of unnecessary words—words that do not improve the reader's understanding of a sentence. Avoid using many words when one or two will serve.

The envelope containing the electric bill was delivered today. (nine words)
The electric bill came today. (five words)

Avoid overuse of the passive voice.

The work done by the carpenter was finished. (eight words)
The carpenter finished the work. (five words)

Revise long sentences to achieve concision.

I wish to say that I have not at this moment fully engaged in this warlike action. (seventeen words)
I have not yet begun to fight. (seven words)

Avoid dependence on *it is, there is,* and *there are.*

It was John Glenn who first orbited the earth in space.
John Glenn first orbited the earth in space.
There are some medicines that have dangerous side effects.
Some medicines have dangerous side effects.

REPETITION

Avoid excessive repetition of words, synonyms, and sounds.

The book on the table is a book about buccaneers in the South Seas.
The book on the table is about buccaneers in the South Seas.
The wind sifted sparks from the sizzling blaze.
The wind blew sparks from the blaze.

16.1 The Dictionary and Usage

■ *Look up each word in parentheses in a current dictionary to determine the correct choice. Underline the answer and write a summary of the usage rule under each sentence.*

EXAMPLE

The television (medium, media) has benefited greatly from satellite broadcasting.

medium; refers to one kind of communication method
media; plural form for more than one kind

1. One of the worst effects of the earthquake, (beside, besides) the general destruction, was the devastating fire.

   _____

   _____

   _____

2. Incoming freshmen are counseled to (try and, try to) attend the orientation seminar.

   _____

   _____

3. A large (amount, number) of monkeys escaped from the enclosure when the zookeeper neglected to lock the gate.

   _____

   _____

   _____

4. After eating *sushi,* a Japanese specialty made of raw fish, the tourist complained that she did not feel (good, well).

   _____

   _____

   _____

5. According to the booklet a carefully written résumé, neat clothing, and a pleasant manner are the (criterion, criteria) for a successful job interview.

_____

_____

_____

6. Shakespeare asks in one of his sonnets whether he should compare his love (to, with) a summer's day.

_____

_____

_____

7. To prepare for her senior recital, the flutist practiced diligently (everyday, every day).

_____

_____

_____

8. Possessing only one horn said to have magical powers, the fabled unicorn was a (unique, most unique) creature.

_____

_____

_____

9. The debater who (inferred, implied) that his opponent was poorly prepared was disqualified for making personal remarks.

_____

_____

_____

10. The kangaroo is one (kind of, kind of a) marsupial found only in Australia.

_____

_____

16.2 The Dictionary and Usage

■ *Look up each word in parentheses in a current dictionary to determine the correct choice. Underline the answer and write a summary of the usage rule under each sentence.*

1. The incumbent, who received (less, fewer) votes than her opponent, clearly had forfeited the trust of the electorate.

   _____

   _____

   _____

2. Unshaven and red-eyed, the newspaper editor looked (as if, like) he had worked for days without sleep.

   _____

   _____

   _____

3. The flowerpot fell (off, off of) the ledge and smashed on the sidewalk.

   _____

   _____

   _____

4. At the turn of the century only a small (percent, percentage) of people owned automobiles.

   _____

   _____

   _____

5. The reason Nero Wolfe is a successful detective is (because, that) he enjoys solving intricate, logical puzzles.

   _____

6. The accident victim was only (partly, partially) covered by insurance.

_____

_____

_____

7. For the coffee merchant, inhaling the aroma of the Colombian beans was a (sensuous, sensual) pleasure.

_____

_____

_____

8. The cache of arrowheads indicated that (sometime, some time) in the past a tribe of primitive Indians had encamped on the banks of the river.

_____

_____

_____

9. The customer complained that (these kinds, these kind) of socks stretched out of shape after the first washing.

_____

_____

_____

10. Soaring in ever-widening circles, the falcon flew (farther, further) than the eye could see.

_____

_____

_____

NAME _____

DATE _____ SCORE _____

16.3 The Dictionary and Usage

■ *Look up each word in parentheses in a current dictionary to determine the correct choice. Underline the answer and write a summary of the usage rule under each sentence.*

1. The Boy Scouts were (already, all ready) to leave when the camp bus arrived.

   _____

   _____

   _____

2. The sobbing child asked the police officer (where her father was, where her father was at).

   _____

   _____

   _____

3. The rock star had so great an (affect, effect) on his audience that three people fainted.

   _____

   _____

   _____

4. The contractor (agreed to, agreed with) the replacement of the kitchen floor.

   _____

   _____

   _____

5. The seven-layer chocolate cake proved (altogether, all together) irresistible to the dieter.

   _____

6. The hot, thirsty campers saw the glimmer of a waterfall a long (way, ways) off.

7. Although she was trained in cellular biology, the graduate student found it difficult to distinguish (among, between) three species of bacteria.

8. After studying for (awhile, a while), the students ordered a pizza.

9. The author felt so (bad, badly) after the disappointing reviews of his book that he vowed never to write again.

10. The audience laughed as the clown (busted, burst, bursted) the balloon.

16.4 The Dictionary and Usage

■ *Look up each word in parentheses in a current dictionary to determine the correct choice. Underline the answer and write a summary of the usage rule under each sentence.*

1. After a local referendum the dome of the (capital, capitol) building was cleaned and repaired.

   _____

   _____

   _____

2. The cheerleaders were so (enthused, enthusiastic) about the touchdown that they performed double somersaults.

   _____

   _____

   _____

3. After being rescued from the burning house, the family pets were frightened, but (alright, all right).

   _____

   _____

   _____

4. Because of a shortage of bamboo shoots, (fewer, less) pandas than expected will survive a severe winter.

   _____

   _____

   _____

5. The theater manager was eager to (finalize, formalize) a salary agreement with the orchestra before the strike deadline.

   _____

_____

_____

6. The interior designer (complemented, complimented) the blue sofa with a green and turquoise rug.

_____

_____

_____

7. The farmer successfully grew a fine crop of corn (being as, because) he installed an extensive sprinkler system.

_____

_____

_____

8. City dwellers grow used to the (continual, continuous) sound of backfiring cars and honking horns.

_____

_____

_____

9. Before the posse (hanged, hung) the outlaw, he was allowed to write a farewell letter to his wife.

_____

_____

_____

10. The producer said that (irregardless, regardless) of the worth of the play, ticket sales would determine the length of its run.

_____

_____

_____

16.5 The Dictionary and Usage

■ *Underline each example of poor usage and write the correction underneath each sentence. No sentence contains more than two such examples. One sentence is correct.*

EXAMPLE

The executive complained that the attempt to *finalize those sort* of deals was frustrating.

formalize; those sorts

1. Compared to an Afghan hound, whose long, fine fur needs careful grooming every day, a German shepherd is easy to care for.

2. The operatic soprano grew so hoarse from the affects of the cold, damp weather that she sang less arias than were included on the program.

3. Because the Capitol was further from their hotel than they remembered, the tourists found themselves wandering through an unfamiliar neighborhood a long ways off from their tour guide.

4. The reason the barbershop quartet performed so many nostalgic numbers is because the audience requested those sort.

5. Going to the circus to see the clown Emmett Kelley perform his unique act—a bumbling attempt to sweep a spotlight into a sack—is the kind of memory to be cherished by the theatergoer.

6. The Ferris wheel whirled all together too fast, like it was about to spin away into the sky.

7. Many superstitions, like the belief in astrological signs, have an affect because the believers are so enthused that they convince themselves.

   _____

8. Fewer than half of the people who attended the opening night of *Aida* wore formal dress; consequently, sequined dresses appeared besides corduroy jeans.

   _____

9. The newspaper reader inferred from the interview that since everyone who ate the chicken salad felt badly, all were suffering from food poisoning.

   _____

10. The student who completed less than half of the problem was given credit for what she had done correctly.

   _____

16.6 The Dictionary and Usage

■ *Underline each example of poor usage and write the correction underneath each sentence. No sentence contains more than two such examples. One sentence is correct.*

1. Many people suffered so badly from smallpox during the eighteenth century that contemporary writers compared the disease with a tidal wave destroying everything in its path.

   _____

2. The theater manager asked the audience to be patient for a while until the leading man, who had fallen off of a ladder, could be replaced by an understudy.

   _____

3. The reviewer implied that audiences at the turn of the century were naive because they enjoyed the kind of a play known as melodrama.

   _____

4. The criteria used by the testing agency to establish new tire safety involves determining the amount of air pressure that will bust a tire.

   _____

5. Of the three kittens the red tabby was the first to try and climb out of the box in order to see where its mother was.

   _____

6. Surveys show that a large percent of televisions are left on all day, everyday.

   _____

7. Because of the unnaturally warm weather, a large amount of camellias were already to bloom before the frost.

   _____

8. The reason the water pump will not work is because it has not been used for some time.

_____

9. Hanging from the ceiling at the party was a *piñata*, a colorful paper ball that, when bursted, showered candies and small toys between the laughing children.

_____

10. The continually barking dog scared away the burglar.

_____

16.7   The Dictionary and Usage

■ *Underline each example of poor usage and write the corrections above each line.*

One of the most exciting events of the nineteenth century was a rather unique industrial world's fair held in the Crystal Palace in London, a glass building that looked all together fragile but was, in fact, very strong. A large percent of the populace were so enthused about the display that some attended the show several times. Inside the transparent building they were treated to extensive displays of machinery and furniture; textiles were hanged from the ceiling, and exotic plants were clustered in small groups all the ways down the central aisle. It was difficult for the viewer to try and choose between the hundreds of exhibits, all so plentiful and so highly decorated that they had a dazzling affect on the eyes.

16.8 The Dictionary and Usage

■ *Underline each example of poor usage and write the corrections above each line.*

A large amount of people would agree to the idea that going to the
circus was an exciting childhood event. The atmosphere itself had a
special tang; even the sawdust hanging in the air was a sensual pleasure as if, for awhile, one could both smell and taste the excitement.
What a thrill it was when the lights went down and the trapeze artist
flew over the crowds like a bird on the wing, and how the audience
jumped when the clown suddenly bursted a balloon filled with water!
Surely nothing can compare to the heart-stopping experience of seeing the unprotected lion tamer taunting the king of the beasts, who,
snarling and growling, was ready to hurl himself off of the ledge in
his cage. Irregardless of the time, the end always came too quickly;
parents were already to leave while children still sat starry-eyed,
clutching the remains of sticky candy apples or crumpled bags of
popcorn.

16.9 The Dictionary and Standard English

■ *With the aid of a dictionary, label the italicized words as* **formal, informal, colloquial,** *and so on. Replace substandard expressions with equivalents in standard English.*

EXAMPLE
The businessman *figured* that he could weather the reces-
sion by prudent investments.

informal;
concluded

1. Many people consider a legislator who votes his
   conscience to be a *patsy.*   _____

2. The Lincoln Memorial is *mighty* impressive any
   time but especially at night when the crowds
   have departed.   _____

3. One can earn *plenty* of extra income by selling
   scrap aluminum.   _____

4. Occasionally some misguided *punks* vandalize
   public property.   _____

5. The irate coach, *annoyed* by questionable decisions by the officials, decided to protest.   _____

6. The fear of *bombing out* on an examination may
   cause a poor performance.   _____

7. *Bugged* by the heavy traffic along the interstate
   highways, some travelers prefer the more tran-
   quil routes of older, two-lane roads.   _____

8. I was certainly *put out* by her rude behavior.   _____

9. I don't want to *wrangle* with you over this mat-
   ter, but I think you are wrong.   _____

10. Something *fishy* is going on here, and I feel un-
    comfortable.   _____

16.10 The Dictionary and Standard English

■ *For each of the following supply an appropriate expression in standard English.*

EXAMPLE

flaky *not dependable* _____

1. they's _____

2. whodunit _____

3. dippy _____

4. gaga _____

5. goldbrick _____

6. gob (three possible answers) _____

7. gent _____

8. guy _____

9. enthused _____

10. goes to show _____

11. hock _____

12. near enough of _____

13. rap _____

14. would not of _____

15. pan out _____

16. set around _____

17. could of _____

18. irregardless _____

19. being as _____

20. suspicioned _____

16.11 Improprieties

■ *Circle improprieties in the following phrases and correct them in the blanks at the right. If you find none, write C in the blank.*

EXAMPLE

(occupation) hazards ___*occupational*_____

1. reforming institution policies _____

2. especial nice _____

3. goulash stew _____

4. education experience _____

5. trivia incident _____

6. a wood mallet _____

7. a wood baseball bat _____

8. a frivolity conversation _____

9. a utopia hideaway _____

10. a utilize room complete with workbench _____

11. the unstabled chemical compounds _____

12. the unskill labor force _____

13. the vandals who rapined Rome _____

14. an erupting volcano crevassing the hills _____

15. criticism writing _____

16. abstracted beyond understanding _____

17. classified as an absorbent _____

18. a handwriting letter _____

19. banjoed their way to the top ten _____

20. a meander stream _____

21. hoboing across the country _____

22. holidayed the time away _____

23. the redirective coming from the officer _____

24. grain-fed slaughter cattle _____

25. ivy tendoned to the walls _____

16.12 Improprieties

■ *Choose the correct word and write it in the blank at the right. Consult a dictionary if necessary.*

EXAMPLE
Only (two, to, too) species of the cat family are presently facing possible extinction in India—the Asian lion and the Bengal tiger.

two

1. She tried to (immolate, emulate) her friend's success at the office.

_____

2. John had a (bailful, baleful) look after the test.

_____

3. All her efforts to diet were (waisted, wasted).

_____

4. My doctor gave me an (emolument, emollient) for my burned hand.

_____

5. Money was available to (aid, aide) me when I could not finish my report.

_____

6. He has always been a rather (obstinate, abstinent) drinker.

_____

7. Never bow to (pier, peer) pressure.

_____

8. The speaker (diluted, alluded) to several books I had never read.

_____

9. She made an (object, abject) apology for her behavior.

_____

10. The banquet was a real (fete, feat).

_____

11. Many begin their vacation under the (allusion, delusion) that they must first burn before they can tan.

_____

12. The sun can burn human skin even on cloudy days; (its, it's) ultraviolet rays easily penetrate cloud cover.

_____

13. The dieter tried to reduce his (wasteline, waistline).

_____

14. The coaching staff of some football teams hire professional psychologists to help motivate (their, there) players.

_____

15. Setting a new record at the marathon was a great (fete, feat) for the runner.

_____

16. (Altering, Altaring) the natural cycle of a forest's development can damage valuable watersheds.

_____

17. (Passed, Past) over by all the political pundits, the darkhorse candidate emerged the winner of the state primary.

_____

18. (Preceding, Proceeding) along migratory routes, wild geese often fly in easily recognizable formations.

_____

19. Physicians (prescribe, proscribe) antibiotics for most respiratory infections.

_____

20. Rapid eye movement indicates continued (psychic, physic) activity after the coming of sleep.

_____

21. Research in (sensual, sensory) perception has made possible the successful teaching of the mentally retarded.

_____

22. The general (moral, morale) of the nation usually increases after a presidential election.

_____

23. The delighted parents welcomed their son's (fiancé, fiancée) with warmth and affection.

_____

24. The city was (greatful, grateful) for the contributions to the library fund.

_____

25. The law rarely accepts the argument that the individual's (conscience, conscious) should be the guide to acceptable social behavior.

_____

16.13 Improprieties

■ *Choose the correct word and write it in the blank at the right. Consult a dictionary if necessary.*

EXAMPLE
(There, Their) haste was unnecessary.

Their

1. After her coronation, she (reined, reigned) for the remainder of the year.

   _____

2. The speaker made a (moot, mute) point in his lecture.

   _____

3. Her (overt, covert) attempt to disrupt the meeting by constantly raising questions was obvious.

   _____

4. We had to (leach, leech) the material to remove the spot.

   _____

5. A good salad often has (leeks, leaks) in it.

   _____

6. He (miens, means) well.

   _____

7. The interest on her account (accrued, acrewed) rapidly.

   _____

8. This is (to, too) much.

   _____

9. My bonus was larger (then, than) I had expected.

   _____

10. The two rams (abutted, butted) heads.

    _____

11. The (plane, plain) the cowboys crossed extends across most of two states.

    _____

12. I hate to see someone (flout, flaunt) wealth.

    _____

13. The new producer has recruited writers throughout the region and claims they write good (material, materiel).

    _____

14. Who is the next of (ken, kin)?

    _____

15. Her story doesn't (gibe, jibe) with the truth.

    _____

16. Many people reject (corporal, corporeal) punishment.

_____

17. The legislators met at the (capital, capitol) rotunda.

_____

18. He was immediately struck by an (instinctive, intuitive) understanding of the problem and the way to solve it.

_____

19. The American language obtains many (lonewords, loanwords) from other languages.

_____

20. The passenger paid her (fare, fair) and walked to a seat on the bus.

_____

21. The building (site, cite) overlooked the park.

_____

22. When the golfer hit the ball into the woods, he cried out, "(Four, Fore)!"

_____

23. The magazine took a (pole, poll) to find out who was the most popular movie star.

_____

24. The Academic (Council, Counsel) discussed the new curriculum.

_____

25. When the driver's car stalled, she quickly placed (flairs, flares) on the highway.

_____

NAME _____

DATE _____ SCORE _____

16.14 Idioms

■ *Circle faulty idioms in the following sentences. Write correct idioms in the blanks at the right.*

EXAMPLE
Presidential and vice-presidential candidates ideally should feel compatible (to) each other.   *with*

1. In the year of 1922 T. S. Eliot published one of the most influential poems of the century.   _____

2. Contrary with prevailing opinion, most Americans really care very much about the health of their cities.   _____

3. Oblivious of possible dangers, the unpredictable grizzly will charge even a man.   _____

4. Many teachers find that attractive classrooms are conducive of learning.   _____

5. The puma and the wolf were once indigenous of almost every state in the union.   _____

6. The coming election has a bearing with almost all Congressional action.   _____

7. Americans' replies to the challenges of periods of crisis usually are of the affirmative.   _____

8. "The dye is cast," the leader said.   _____

9. I read the book from cover to conclusion.   _____

10. That problem is water over the bridge now.   _____

16.15 Idioms

■ *Circle faulty idioms in the following sentences. Write correct idioms in the blanks at the right. Write C if the idiom is correct.*

EXAMPLE
This book compares computers (with) the human brain.   *to*

1. I am fond for rare steaks for dinner.   _____

2. We jointed the two pieces of steel.   _____

3. The parents doted in their children.   _____

4. We decided to turn away the offer on our home.   _____

5. I insisted in another chance.   _____

6. When it comes to playing tennis, I am superior over everyone in my class.   _____

7. The trip was not all that interesting.   _____

8. The reason the dam broke is because of the heavy spring rains.   _____

9. In regards to the city's problems, the mayor will call a council meeting.   _____

10. Political candidates often win elections by using their ability to charm and flatter the voters.   _____

16.16 Triteness

■ *Revise the following sentences to eliminate triteness.*

EXAMPLE
Our two managers are like two peas in a pod.

Our two managers are close friends.

1. He fought the good fight but was doomed to defeat.

   _____

   _____

2. She was a fair-weather friend who was never around in the clinches.

   _____

   _____

3. Jim was really burning up the highway until he was stopped by two of the boys in blue.

   _____

   _____

4. "You have bought during a declining market," said the doleful stockbroker to her disheartened client, "but if at first you don't succeed, try, try again."

   _____

   _____

   _____

5. San Francisco, a city that was rebuilt after suffering the effects of a devastating earthquake, is proof that every cloud has a silver lining.

   _____

_____

_____

6. Old diaries, journals, and letters reveal that the early pioneers in the West found some of the wild country to be pretty as a picture.

_____

_____

_____

7. The chief targets of confidence men are gullible investors who continue to believe that there is a pot of gold at the end of the rainbow.

_____

_____

_____

8. While traveling down the highway of life, one must remember that virtue is its own reward.

_____

_____

_____

9. The thrust of most economists' complaints is that short-range political considerations take precedence over long-range economic policy.

_____

_____

_____

10. The premises of international diplomacy are that the pen is mightier than the sword and that a soft answer turneth away wrath.

_____

_____

_____

16.17 Triteness

■ *Revise the following sentences to eliminate triteness.*

EXAMPLE
Everyone on the team was happy as a lark.

Everyone on the team was pleased with the victory.

1. Famous authors are often considered to be sharp as a tack.

   _____

   _____

2. The United States traditionally has been in the forefront of medical research.

   _____

   _____

   _____

3. Superstars of the college sports scene, in a manner of speaking, can write their own tickets in professional sports.

   _____

   _____

4. The first British colonists in America quickly learned that charity and neighborliness were necessary to keep the ball rolling.

   _____

   _____

   _____

5. A few of these first colonists gave up the ship and returned to England, but most never lost heart.

   _____

_____

_____

6. Those willing to travel in the wee hours of the morning usually spend less for airline fares.

_____

_____

_____

7. We cut our traces and hit the road to our new home in Muleshoe, Texas.

_____

_____

_____

8. The main duty of the public health officer is to nip communicable diseases in the bud.

_____

_____

_____

9. Mary threw salt on his wound and caused him to have a hangdog look.

_____

_____

_____

10. The batter slammed the ball into the outfield, raced to first, and then cut for second, running at lightning speed.

_____

_____

_____

NAME _____

DATE _____ SCORE _____

16.18 Wordiness

■ *Revise the following sentences to make them concise.*

EXAMPLE
~~In her time~~ Marie Curie was one of the most important persons of her age.

1. It was William Harvey who first wrote about the circulation of the blood.

   _____

   _____

   _____

2. The music that he played pleased the people in the audience.

   _____

   _____

   _____

3. To be sure, Benjamin Franklin was not, as it were, a great writer, but he was, to all intents and purposes, a great man, more or less.

   _____

   _____

   _____

4. Americans have always applauded the tenacious underdog who is down but who tries to recover and help himself.

   _____

   _____

   _____

5. All human beings possess certain doctrines of natural rights which have been instituted by nature.

   _____

6. As anybody can see, most Americans have been affected by television in such a way that their appreciation of the arts has obviously become less and less.

_____

_____

_____

7. In comparing college with high school, from both the educational and the social standpoints, one will find there are indeed many differences.

_____

_____

8. In the times in which we live, a man just can hardly be independent any longer. Look what is happening to him in the field of education. People virtually dictate to him about his economic theories. This is also true even in his personal philosophy of life.

_____

_____

_____

9. Looking out the window of our car, we saw the little, tiny cafe you had told us about in the letter you sent us.

_____

_____

_____

10. After reviewing the evidence in your case that was presented by your lawyer to me, we realize that there is some justification and warrant for a new trial.

_____

_____

_____

16.19 Wordiness

■ *Revise the following sentences to make them concise.*

EXAMPLE

I came for the reason that I was hungry.

I came because I was hungry. _____

1. In this day and age in the world in which we live, we face enormously large economic problems.

   _____

   _____

2. We went to the library at our school to gather books, articles, and research material for our term papers.

   _____

   _____

3. The author's writings contain many short, brief sentences that express broad, basic truths and are very readable.

   _____

   _____

4. No one can deny that hunting big game with a camera is fully as dangerous as hunting big game with a rifle.

   _____

   _____

5. An ovenbird is an American bird which is a member of the warbler family and which builds a nest that resembles an oven on the floor of a forest.

   _____

   _____

   _____

6. In many ways certain cities retained and still do retain a small-town atmosphere in those neighborhoods characterized by unique ethnic charm and lifestyles.

   _____

   _____

   _____

7. For years and years the basic cultural foundation of this great nation was the small town with its small, homogeneous neighborhoods and communal cohesion.

   _____

   _____

   _____

8. Beginning in the 1930s and continuing through several decades down to the present time, writers have often been interested in Hollywood as a setting for their novels.

   _____

   _____

   _____

9. The water that overflowed from the plumbing in our bathroom reached the hall carpet and caused a stain on it.

   _____

   _____

   _____

10. Two breeds of dogs that are generally considered by most authorities as good guard dogs are the Doberman pinscher and the German shepherd, and these two breeds may, without difficulty, be compared and contrasted on the grounds of appearance, disposition, and physical prowess.

    _____

    _____

    _____

16.20 Wordiness

■ *Revise the following sentences to make them concise.*

1. It is a known and proven fact that run-off elections draw fewer voters than regular elections.

    _____

    _____

    _____

2. We are not of the opinion that we are in favor of the ideas presented by the committee.

    _____

    _____

    _____

3. Let us end the festivities of the evening by all singing the song of our school.

    _____

    _____

    _____

4. Current research on the nervous system of the cockroach, of all things, might just conceivably lead to a cure for glaucoma, a disease of the eye.

    _____

    _____

    _____

5. Major political pollsters are presently worried about the definite trend of so many people to refuse to answer questionnaires or to take part in interviews.

    _____

6. Some birdfeeders differ in various ways from others because various birds have different eating habits and feeding requirements, and it is just that simple.

7. Mammoths were prehistoric beasts that looked like elephants with very hairy skin and that often measured eleven feet at the shoulders with tusks as long as thirteen feet.

8. Laws requiring motorcycle riders to wear crash helmets have saved, beyond any doubt or question, many lives in the past and will most certainly account for the saving of many lives in the future.

9. Our present-day, or Gregorian, calendar is based on the Julian calendar, which was established by the famous Roman emperor Julius Caesar and which fixed the length of the year at 365 days.

10. The teacher of English we had during this term required each of us to read several of the books from a list she gave everyone to examine.

16.21 Repetition

■ *Revise the following sentences to eliminate ineffective repetition.*

EXAMPLE

The director watched her wrist watch continually during the dress rehearsal.

The director carefully timed the dress rehearsal.

(modified to eliminate repetition of *watched* and *watch* and of the *w* sound)

1. Instant replays show that officials usually make correct calls and perform their duties both correctly and responsibly.

   _____

   _____

   _____

2. After the bear market of the early 1970s, stockbrokers decided to diversify and to market various other securities other than common stocks.

   _____

   _____

   _____

3. The danger of dense cloud cover in densely traveled air corridors is a midair collision.

   _____

   _____

   _____

4. Most large cities are circumscribed by large beltways that prevent large traffic jams.

   _____

   _____

   _____

5. The situation comedy that is interesting, engaging, and prepossessing will always attract and engage a television audience.

_____

_____

6. The respected judge of a debate never allows contempt or scorn or disparagement or derision to be displayed on the debate floor.

_____

_____

_____

7. Sewing one's own clothes is a way of saving money and allows one to choose one's favorite style and one's favorite fabric.

_____

_____

_____

8. Successful football teams that win often have kickers who kick field goals and kick extra points well.

_____

_____

_____

9. The alert insurance adjustor must be constantly alert to improper evidence of impropriety or fraud, while never forgetting to be fair, equitable, and just.

_____

_____

_____

10. Farmers' markets are enjoying a good resurgence in larger cities; on good days, a farmer in New York or Seattle or Santa Fe or Boston may gross a thousand dollars.

_____

_____

_____

16.22 Repetition

■ *Revise the following sentences to eliminate ineffective repetition.*

EXAMPLE
Producers who *produce* useful *products* stay in business.

Manufacturers of useful products stay in business.

1. Erupting volcanoes erupt with terrific force, spewing hot, molten lava and scattering volcanic ash for miles and miles and miles.

   _____

   _____

2. Floods that flood fields and flood croplands are ever-present dangers to the farmer.

   _____

   _____

3. Powdery snow on ski slopes must be monitored constantly for loose powdery density and possible snowslides.

   _____

   _____

   _____

4. Small bark beetles bear a fungus that causes a disease which attacks the Dutch elm tree.

   _____

   _____

   _____

5. Fashion designers sometimes fashion their designs after the traditional dress of nomadic tribes.

   _____

_____

_____

6. Horizontal stripes on clothes emphasize heaviness and are shunned by heavy people.

_____

_____

_____

7. The climbing high prices of new cars will climb higher and higher before they level off.

_____

_____

_____

8. Sand painting, the ancient art of painting pictures with colored sand, was first originated by American Indians for their ancient rituals.

_____

_____

_____

9. Some elk from overpopulated elk herds in Yellowstone National Park have been exported to other parks in other regions and even to other countries.

_____

_____

_____

10. Charcoal, first used as a filter in gas masks during the First World War, filters the air in submarines and spacecraft and also filters automobile emissions.

_____

_____

_____

Connotation, Figurative Language, and Vocabulary

CONNOTATION

Words often have special associations and meanings called **connotations.** **Denotations** of words are their precise meanings. Denotatively, the word *home* simply refers to a dwelling place. Connotatively, the word suggests several emotional reactions relating to family, friends, and special occasions.

Good writers attempt to find words that have the right associations—those that work most effectively.

EXAMPLE

Fred is a *funny* person. (*Funny* is weak because it is too general.)

IMPROVED

Fred is *witty*.

Fred is a *practical joker*.

Fred is a *great impersonator*.

FIGURATIVE LANGUAGE

Avoid mixed and inappropriate figures of speech. Mixed figures associate things that are not logically related.

EXAMPLE

He stumbled along like a car in heavy traffic. (Cars cannot *stumble*.)

IMPROVED

He stumbled along like a wounded soldier.

Use figurative comparisons to create originality.

EXAMPLE

Language is the cornerstone of civilization. (metaphor)

Opportunity is *like* a good mystery story; you never know what will happen when you turn the page. (simile)

FLOWERY LANGUAGE

Avoid ornate or pretentious language. Make your sentences clear.

PLAIN LANGUAGE	FLOWERY LANGUAGE
today	in this world in which we live and work
pen	this writing instrument
finally	having reached the termination of this discourse

17.1 Connotation

■ *Words which have approximately the same denotation frequently suggest meanings that are different. The combinations that follow bring together words with different connotations. In the spaces at the right, rate each word in terms of its favorability of connotation—1 for most favorable, 2 for less favorable, and 3 for least favorable. Be prepared to defend your decisions and to explain the different shades of connotation.*

EXAMPLE

offhand _____2_____

thoughtless _____3_____

casual _____1_____

1. prudent	_____	6. uncertain	_____
careful	_____	insecure	_____
cautious	_____	desperate	_____
2. perilous	_____	7. absurd	_____
dangerous	_____	silly	_____
scary	_____	preposterous	_____
3. demanded	_____	8. talented	_____
requested	_____	capable	_____
wanted	_____	competent	_____
4. dislike	_____	9. quiet	_____
disapprove	_____	restful	_____
detest	_____	serene	_____
5. like	_____	10. rile	_____
adore	_____	peeve	_____
appreciate	_____	anger	_____

11. wither _____   19. vulture _____

   languish _____   scavenger _____

   shrivel _____   buzzard _____

12. simple _____   20. boat _____

   naive _____   ship _____

   innocent _____   liner _____

13. impulsive _____   21. lie _____

   spontaneous _____   deception _____

   unconstrained _____ falsehood _____

14. famous _____   22. visionary _____

   notorious _____   dreamer _____

   well-known _____   romantic _____

15. aged _____   23. illegal _____

   mellow _____   unlawful _____

   mature _____   criminal _____

16. food _____   24. ignoble _____

   meat _____   vile _____

   victuals _____   disreputable _____

17. automobile _____ 25. request _____

   car _____   solicit _____

   limousine _____   beg _____

18. singer _____

   vocalist _____

   virtuoso _____

17.2 Connotation

■ *Words which have approximately the same denotation frequently suggest meanings that are different. The combinations that follow bring together words with different connotations. In the spaces at the right, rate each word in terms of its favorability of connotation—1 for most favorable, 2 for less favorable, and 3 for least favorable. Be prepared to defend your decisions and to explain the different shades of connotation.*

EXAMPLE

earnings _____1_____

profits _____3_____

gains _____2_____

1. force _____   6. part _____

   compel _____   separate _____

   coerce _____   sever _____

2. miscellaneous _____   7. intentions _____

   motley _____   design _____

   assorted _____   end _____

3. offensive _____   8. ration _____

   repulsive _____   dole _____

   revolting _____   pittance _____

4. haggard _____   9. motive _____

   cadaverous _____   incentive _____

   wasted _____   inducement _____

5. redeem _____   10. clothed _____

   aid _____   attired _____

   save _____   dressed _____

11. awkward   _____

    bungling   _____

    incompetent   _____

12. dress   _____

    frock   _____

    gown   _____

13. puny   _____

    little   _____

    small   _____

14. plead   _____

    argue   _____

    exhort   _____

15. angry   _____

    mad   _____

    wrathful   _____

16. resist   _____

    defy   _____

    oppose   _____

17. distinguished   _____

    noted   _____

    renowned   _____

18. wealthy   _____

    rich   _____

    opulent   _____

19. probity   _____

    candor   _____

    frankness   _____

20. horde   _____

    crowd   _____

    mob   _____

21. alarming   _____

    frightful   _____

    scary   _____

22. fat   _____

    obese   _____

    corpulent   _____

23. imitation   _____

    counterfeit   _____

    sham   _____

24. perseverance   _____

    obstinacy   _____

    doggedness   _____

25. merchandise   _____

    hawk   _____

    peddle   _____

NAME _____

DATE _____ SCORE _____

17.3 Figurative Language

■ *Here is a descriptive passage from Francis Parkman's* The Oregon Trail. *Fill in the blanks using the following list of Parkman's figures of speech and images.*

bellowed and growled	accompaniment	to roll hoarsely
whirling sheets	beat down	leaped out quivering
cataracts	black heads	long rolling peal
	deep muttering	piles of cotton

It was late that morning before we were on the march; and early in the afternoon we were compelled to encamp, for a thunder-gust came up and suddenly enveloped us in [1] _____ of rain. With much ado we pitched our tents amid the tempest, and all night long the thunder [2] _____ over our heads. In the morning light peaceful showers succeeded the [3] _____ of rain, that had been drenching us through the canvas of our tents. About noon, when there were some treacherous indications of fair weather, we got in motion again.

Not a breath of air stirred over the free and open prairie; the clouds were like light [4] _____; and where the blue sky was visible, it wore a hazy and languid aspect. The sun [5] _____ upon us with a sultry, penetrating heat almost insupportable, and as our party crept slowly along over the interminable levels the horses hung their heads as they waded fetlock deep through the mud, and the men slouched into the easiest position upon the saddle. At last, towards evening, the old familiar [6] _____ of thunder-clouds rose fast above the horizon, and the same [7] _____ of distant thunder that had become the ordinary [8] _____ of our afternoon's journey began [9] _____ over the prairie. Only a few minutes elapsed before the whole sky was densely shrouded, and the prairie and some clusters of woods in front assumed a purple hue beneath the inky shadows. Suddenly from the densest fold of the cloud the flash [10] _____ again and again down to the edge of the prairie; and at the same instant came the sharp burst and the [11] _____ of the thunder. A cool wind, filled with the smell of rain, just then overtook us, levelling the tall grass by the side of the path.

17.4 Flowery Language

■ *Revise the following sentences to eliminate flowery language.*

EXAMPLE
The inside of a geode glitters with the silvery radiance of sidereal splendor.

The inside of a geode sparkles with crystals.

1. We looked at the puffy cotton balls in the sky.

   _____

   _____

2. Two Herculean Adonises vied in the ultimate confrontations of the Mr. Universe competition.

   _____

   _____

3. Many cardiologists advise a swift retreat from the ambrosial condiments of the evening repast.

   _____

   _____

   _____

4. Elegant garbs of sartorial splendor often disguise patrician parsimony.

   _____

   _____

5. Many poets have been inspired by the vision of artless, cherubic children gamboling like sylvan nymphs over the verdurous sward.

   _____

6. With the coming of golden autumn the cultivators of the earth garner the blessings of Ceres.

_____

_____

_____

7. The vererable institution of holy matrimony has become the object of much sociological research in the hallowed halls of academia.

_____

_____

_____

8. Rafters down the mighty Mississippi watercourse provide the sonorous, nocturnal chorus of bullfrogs with a spirited audience.

_____

_____

_____

9. The pied clouds of pastel hues served notice that the strong winds had given way to the wings of gentle zephyrs.

_____

_____

_____

10. The lofty reaches of the craggy tops of the mountains were covered by the freezing precipitation that fell in a frenzied swirl.

_____

_____

_____

17.5 Vocabulary

■ *In the blank at the right, place the letter of the word or phrase you believe is nearest in meaning to the italicized word. You may guess; then consult a dictionary.*

EXAMPLE

He has a *paramour:* (a) small tractor, (b) virtue, (c) illicit lover   *C*

1. a *defunct* issue: (a) overdrawn, (b) boring, (c) dead   _____

2. an *assiduous* student: (a) diligent, (b) well-read, (c) skeptical   _____

3. an *innocuous* potion: (a) poisonous, (b) harmless, (c) powerful   _____

4. a *quixotic* character: (a) questioning, (b) variable, (c) visionary   _____

5. a *lethargic* river: (a) sluggish, (b) polluted, (c) deep   _____

6. a *niggardly* church member: (a) prejudiced, (b) stingy, (c) swarthy   _____

7. the *nadir* of my life: (a) abomination, (b) highest point, (c) lowest point   _____

8. a *gratuitous* insult: (a) unwarranted, (b) deserved, (c) vehement   _____

9. their *heterodox* beliefs: (a) spiritual, (b) conservative, (c) heretical   _____

10. a *verbose* lecturer: (a) dynamic, (b) wordy, (c) boring   _____

11. please *elucidate*: (a) explain, (b) denounce, (c) arrange   _____

12. an *omnivorous* being: (a) immortal, (b) eating all kinds of food, (c) knowing everything   _____

13. Behold the *firmament*: (a) earth, (b) sky, (c) fortification

14. to *opt* for freedom: (a) decide, (b) flee, (c) sing

15. a *disparate* group of people: (a) essentially different, (b) dangerous, (c) capable of murder

16. a *proletarian*: (a) wage-earner, (b) revolutionary, (c) democrat

17. a *laconic* reply: (a) heated, (b) ill-advised, (c) concise

18. an *exigent* situation: (a) demanding, (b) deceased, (c) absent

19. the beloved *prelate*: (a) actor, (b) grandparent, (c) church dignitary

20. a *choleric* temperament: (a) sickly, (b) irascible, (c) morose

17.6 Vocabulary

■ *In the blank at the right, place the letter of the word or phrase you believe is nearest in meaning to the italicized word. You may guess; then consult a dictionary.*

EXAMPLE

He gave a *specious* answer to the question: (a) special,
(b) unusual, (c) questionable   _____C_____

1. an *aquiline* nose: (a) hooked, (b) long, (c) snub   _____

2. *desultory* talk: (a) insulting, (b) boring, (c) random   _____

3. a *malignant* plan: (a) ineffective, (b) evil, (c) terminal   _____

4. an *overt* act: (a) subversive, (b) hostile, (c) open to view   _____

5. a hunched *Mephistopheles*: (a) ogre, (b) devil, (c) Greek god   _____

6. a *crucial* year: (a) disturbing, (b) painful, (c) decisive   _____

7. a needed *admonition*: (a) reproof, (b) falsehood, (c) compliment   _____

8. a *facetious* remark: (a) obvious, (b) witty, (c) angry   _____

9. a *voluptuous* woman: (a) sensual, (b) plump, (c) adulterous   _____

10. the *acrimonious* controversy: (a) bitter, (b) marital, (c) religious   _____

11. an *ineradicable* mark: (a) disfiguring, (b) black, (c) indelible   _____

12. feeling *nauseated*: (a) sickening, (b) sick, (c) ridiculous   _____

13. a *strident* voice: (a) low, (b) shrill, (c) stuttering   _____

14. devices of *propaganda*: (a) spreading ideas,
    (b) lies, (c) politics   _____

15. the *inherent* supremacy of human beings:
    (a) natural, (b) unnatural, (c) immoral   _____

16. an *anachronism*: (a) severe deformity, (b) event
    placed in the wrong time, (c) an enigma   _____

17. a human *fetus*: (a) unborn child, (b) abortion,
    (c) corpse   _____

18. a *swarthy* villain: (a) sneaky, (b) greasy, (c) dark-
    complexioned   _____

19. to *refute* an argument: (a) summarize, (b) dis-
    prove, (c) begin   _____

20. to treat with *levity*: (a) gaiety, (b) seriousness,
    (c) haste   _____

18

Paragraph Unity

NAME _____

DATE _____ SCORE _____

18.1 Topic Sentences

■ *Divide the following passage into paragraphs by inserting the sign ¶. The original passage contains three paragraphs. Underline topic sentences, and in the blanks at the end of the passage, write briefly in your own words the controlling idea of each paragraph.*

If country music, like soul and Latin music, remains a securely delineated subgenre within pop, there are signs of erosion of that purity. The hope, as well as the fear, in Nashville these days is the "crossover," or the leap of a country song onto the national pop sales charts, and hence from relatively modest success to the millions to be made when the big pop AM stations all over the country start playing and propagating a record. The hope is that a country singer can reach that wider acclaim. The fear is that, in so doing, the artist may dilute his style past recognizability. And, further, there is fear that the process can work the other way—the supposed country charts in recent years have often been topped by such artists as John Denver, Olivia Newton-John, and Linda Ronstadt. They may be singing outwardly country songs, but they are hardly country in either their biographies or their links to Nashville musical institutions. The whole crossover phenomenon provides an obvious musical metaphor for Southern culture and its relation to the rest of America: crossover success means recognition on a national level even as the indigenous roots that nourish that success are eroded. Needless to say, many older forms of country music remain vital parts of our folk culture today. What distinguishes them from mainstream country and what helps assure their traditional purity is their very freedom from commercialism. There are some established country stars who consciously revert to the Anglo-American folk tradition that underlies all country music. But the many folk festivals around the country are full of eager "string bands"—fiddle-dominated ensembles that trace their ancestry back through the crudely amplified fiddle groups of the Depression to the traditional country and mountain ensembles of the nineteenth century. This music goes by a variety of overlapping names—"mountain music," "old-timey music"—that often refer to similar music with only minor regional variants. The best-known form of such older music is bluegrass, popularized by Eric Weissberg with his music for the film *Deliverance*. Bluegrass is actually of fairly recent invention, for all its debts to older forms of folkcountry, and its inventors, Bill Monroe and the Bluegrass Boys, are still regaling audiences with their blend of quick-stepping tempos, exuberant fiddle playing, and high, hard tenorizing. More recently, Earl Scruggs, once the banjo-playing half of the Flatt and Scruggs duo, has attempted to broaden bluegrass's appeal by allying it with quasi-rock instrumentation.

—John Rockwell,
"Blues, and Other Noises, in the Night"

CONTROLLING IDEAS

1. _____

_____

2. _____

_____

3. _____

_____

18.2 Topic Sentences

■ *Divide the following passage into paragraphs by inserting the sign ¶. The original passage contains three paragraphs. Underline topic sentences, and in the blanks at the end of the passage, write briefly in your own words the controlling idea of each paragraph.*

After a musical has opened in New York and has had the rare privilege of getting unanimous raves from the critics, everyone from the producers, writers, and directors right on down to the chorus relaxes to bask in the sunlight of critical acceptance, public support, and financial gain. The dancers, especially, enjoy the hit in a strange sort of way. They immediately go back to the strenuous activity of daily jazz and ballet classes, masochistically stretching and twisting in order to stay in shape for auditions when this show eventually closes. After the strenuous activity of daytime classes, the theatre often becomes a place to rest up and recuperate for tomorrow's classes. Out come the magazines, books, knitting, and small change for poker games, and even possibly TV with the sound turned way down; the whole thing takes on the atmosphere of a USO. At this point the management, in the flush of success, decides that it can afford an extra dancer to cover the possibility that dancers will be out sick from time to time.

—Bob Evans,
"How to Get a Job as a 'Swing Dancer' in a Hit Broadway Show"

CONTROLLING IDEAS

1. _____

    _____

2. _____

    _____

3. _____

    _____

NAME _____

DATE _____ SCORE _____

18.3 Topic Sentences

■ *Divide the following passage into paragraphs by inserting the sign ¶. The original passage contains four paragraphs. Underline topic sentences, and in the blanks at the end of the passage, write briefly in your own words the controlling idea of each paragraph.*

The rationales for saving wild species, at the onset of the movement several decades ago, were largely ethical, esthetic, and ecological. These fundamental arguments have since been joined by another, equally important one. We depend on our fellow species for our material welfare, and ultimately for our future survival, in all sorts of unsuspected ways. Conserving the planet's tropical areas is especially important to realizing the utilitarian benefits of wild species. Some 70 percent of the Earth's plants and animals exist in the tropics, which means—by and large—in developing nations. Third World leaders may be personally aware of the ethical and esthetic values of wildlife, but they also recognize that it is politically unfeasible for their impoverished populations to retain space for rhinos, giraffes, and jaguars when millions of hungry people lack land to grow their crops. If wildlife can "pay its way" in the marketplace and make a local economic contribution, then space may yet be found for threatened species. Although some may view the utilitarian rationale for preserving species as a narrow view of wildlife's true value, there need not be a conflict between the consideration of a species' economic contributions and the belief that its continued existence needs no justification. But faced with expanding human populations, especially in developing nations, we must realize there is less and less room for wildlife that exists for its own sake. We use hundreds of products each day that owe their existence to plants and animals. The ways in which wild species support our daily welfare fall under three main headings: agriculture, medicine, and industry.

—Norman Myers,
"By Saving Wild Species, We May Be Saving Ourselves"

CONTROLLING IDEAS

1. _____

   _____

2. _____

   _____

3. _____

_____

4. _____

_____

18.4   Topic Sentences

■ *Divide the following passage into paragraphs by inserting the sign ¶. The original passage contains four paragraphs. Underline topic sentences, and in the blanks at the end of the passage, write briefly in your own words the controlling idea of each paragraph.*

The crucial role of journalism in a democracy is to provide a common ground of knowledge and analysis, a meeting place for national debate: it is the link between people and institutions. Without the information provided by newspapers and TV, citizens would have little basis for deciding what to believe and whom to support. Just as a pervasive mistrust of police could cause a breakdown of order, a growing hostility to the press could sever the ligaments of a workable society. Moreover, without a strong and trusted press, people would have almost no way to keep their government and other big institutions honest. Government, particularly the Federal Establishment, has vast powers to mislead the people and manage the news. Officials can conceal impending actions until their effects are irreversible. Other big institutions—corporations, unions, hospitals, police forces— prefer to cloak their decision-making process and their performance from the scrutiny of the public, whose lives may be deeply affected. And despite the passage of shield laws to protect journalists from having to reveal sources, they are regularly subpoenaed to testify about what they have reported. Journalists became so aggressive partly because they knew, contrary to the widely held public view, that they were Davids fighting Goliaths. As the press itself grows into a more powerful institution, it must be careful how it uses its strength, whether it faces an ordinary individual or a President: the attempt to uncover can too easily turn into the impulse to tear apart. Freedom of the press, like any other freedom, can be dangerous. But Thomas Jefferson, who suffered at the hands of journalists as much as any contemporary politician, insisted that protecting the press at its worst was an essential part of having the press be free.

—William A. Henry III,
"Journalism Under Fire"

CONTROLLING IDEAS

1. _____

_____

2. _____

_____

3. _____

_____

4. _____

_____

18.5 Digressive Sentences

■ *In the blanks at the left, write the number of any sentence that is digressive. In any paragraph there may be as many as three such sentences.*

EXAMPLE

(1) To use a library efficiently one must first learn how books are classified in the computerized catalog. (2) These catalogs are located usually on a library's main floor—but not always. (3) Books are listed in three ways: by author, by title, and by subject. (4) Thus if one knows a title, but not an author or a subject, one can easily locate a book.

_____2_____

A. (1) One of the most overused words today is "major." (2) This is not the army or marine rank. (3) No company would dare list a new program as a "minor" one. (4) And what politician would ever deliver a "short talk"? (5) No, any speech no matter how insignificant must be labeled a "major address to the American people." (6) Thus "major" takes its place alongside "startling new discovery" and the many other expressions that have undermined our language.

_____

B. (1) Financial aid for students includes basic grants, work-study jobs, scholarships, and loans. (2) In the past, students who required financial assistance often had to drop out of school and work for a few months. (3) Many students simultaneously receive aid from several of these sources, usually combining scholarships with work-study programs. (4) College administrations continually solicit alumni for more money. (5) Jobs are especially popular because they may provide valuable experience for a future vocation. (6) Some of the country's most distinguished citizens received scholarships. (7) All students in need of financial assistance qualify for aid in one form or another. (8) Even if they must borrow from university loan funds, they usually pay only minimal interest charges. (9) Students who desire assistance should contact their school's financial aid office for further information.

_____

C. (1) Almost any backyard can be transformed into a showcase wildlife habitat. (2) Birdfeeders, birdbaths, small fishponds—all combined with the right shrubs and trees—will attract a variety of wildlife. (3) Many neighbors may want to transform their yards as well. (4) Now several species of wildlife are steadily losing their natural habitat to industry and agriculture. (5) Shrubs (such as hawthorne, crab apple, and silky dogwood) and hardwood trees (like oak or beech) serve small animals and many songbirds. (6) In addition, colorful annual flowers attract many helpful insects. (7) If enough fresh water is available, ducks, raccoons, frogs, and crayfish will soon visit. (8) Backyard ecology is especially popular among the youth.

D.   (1) To see the Grand Canyon as it should be seen, a visitor must rise before dawn. (2) The canyon is located in northern Arizona. (3) Just before the sun appears the walls of the canyon are a deep purple, and a visitor almost feels the eerie silence. (4) Gradually the canyon comes alive. (5) Soon there are the cries of a few birds. (6) Then with the first streaks of light, the rocks begin to glow in rich oranges and reds. (7) Finally, the details appear—the deep crevices, the patches of grass and mesquite and sage—and a visitor who looks closely may see a deer or chipmunk. (8) Later the visitor can visit the many shops located near Bright Angel Lodge and El Tovar.

E.   (1) The great cities before Rome—Corinth, Carthage, Syracuse—were trading and manufacturing centers. (2) Rome, on the other hand, was the financial and political capital of the Western world. (3) Rome never rivaled previous great cities in commerce or industry. (4) Another great city of the ancient world was Carthage, located in North Africa. (5) Rome usually imported most of its necessities and luxuries from cities and regions under its military and political control. (6) Sicily and Africa especially provided for Rome's agricultural needs such as corn. (7) During the so-called Golden Age of Greece, Athens was the intellectual center of Western civilization.

F.   (1) What does the television mean to the American family? (2) Many people enjoy westerns, comedies, and detective shows. (3) Ask those who work at home what they enjoy on television and learn the sordid details in the lives of every character on "As the World Turns" and "All My Children." (4) Ask any husband which comes first—the news or dinner—and hear how important it is to keep informed by watching Roger Mudd report from Washington. (5) And how many of us have heard some child wail, "I don't have anything to do!" when the TV is at the shop? (6) One can only wonder if our founding fathers ever could have envisioned television as our principal means to achieve "life, liberty, and the pursuit of happiness."

———————

G.   (1) The modern photographer needs more than a simple developing kit to process photographs at home. (2) Actually, processing photographs at home is probably more expensive than having professional laboratories develop them. (3) The most important and most expensive item required for film processing is a good enlarger. (4) If one develops negatives without an enlarger, then the final pictures are almost too small to enjoy. (5) Used enlargers for sale are very difficult to find. (6) Furthermore, one should purchase an enlarging easel, an enlarger timer, and a focusing lens. (7) Only after buying this relatively expensive equipment can the amateur photographer hope to develop good-quality prints.

———————

H.   (1) Many expressions have been used to describe the second half of the twentieth century. (2) With enormous arrogance we have called our brief period of history the nuclear age or the age of progress and cavalierly ignored any improvements in the human lot that were produced over the last several thousand years. (3) Perhaps we should reassess our view of ourselves and look a bit to the world we inherited. (4) Moreover, we have created more waste, expended more of the earth's natural resources, spent more money and time on frivolities and entertainment, and—as far as we can see into the future at this moment—left generations to come with greater problems to solve than any previous generation left to its successors in the entire span of human history. (5) We have proclaimed this the era of progress, but future generations may one day mock us for our vanity. (6) We should all try to improve our environment.

———————

I.   (1) Archaeology is a much more exact science than many people realize. (2) For example, archaeologists have determined that, on a day in late spring approximately 400,000 years ago, about twenty-five people made a brief visit to a cove on the Mediterranean coast near Nice, France. (3) From the study of fossil bones, stone tools, various imprints in the sand, and the density of the sand, scientists have reconstructed in detail much of the three-day sojourn. (4) Imprints give clues to where these ancient people slept and what they slept on. (5) Archaeology has really matured as a science and has become quite popular in the public's eye since Heinrich Schliemann's excavation of ancient cities in the latter nineteenth century. (6) These imaginative scientists also know much about the food these nomadic people ate, how they prepared it, how they hunted for food, and how they protected the group from predators at night. (7) The human imagination simply has no limits.

_____

J.   (1) When people complain about the outlandish fashions of the great contemporary American and French designers, someone should remind them that this is not the only age to flaunt the outrageous in wearing apparel. (2) These clothes may be purchased at most major department stores and in many boutiques across the country. (3) For sheer absurdity we only have to look to the zoot suit of the 1940s, or, if we are truly interested in the bizarre, we might remember the bustle and bloomers. (4) No age has been without its oddities. (5) We can only be thankful that so few of them became permanent additions to our wardrobes.

_____

K.   (1) Public meetings between management and labor can be beneficial. (2) But one should not expect miracles. (3) Formal negotiations also may be detrimental if either side plays only to the press. (4) Informal contacts usually precede public meetings and set agendas. (5) This procedure often reduces the possibility of either side grandstanding for publicity. (6) Indeed, these contacts usually are necessary for productive bargaining.

_____

L.   (1) Successful interviewing for a job requires careful planning. (2) Some study of the prospective employer is necessary. (3) Factual knowledge about a firm or industry impresses personnel managers. (4) One should research the company or firm thoroughly in a library or through personal contacts with other employees. (5) The successful candidate knows the company's goals and makes them his or her own.

_____

M.   (1) Changing patterns of weather may cause dramatic shifts in population. (2) When climates change, land that once was fertile may become desert. (3) People must move or face starvation if they live in areas where irrigation is not possible. (4) Weather and population are inextricably linked. (5) Crops and livestock must have adequate rainfall.

_____

N.   (1) The American bald eagle seems to be making a comeback. (2) Once on the verge of extinction, the eagle now has increased its population throughout most of its range. (3) DDT pollution caused severe problems for the bald eagle. (4) It is now protected by law against hunters. (5) If not healthy, the bald eagle population has at least increased significantly.

_____

O.   (1) The soft drink business is in transition. (2) Recent introduction of no-caffeine colas and of new artificial sweeteners for diet drinks has created new markets. (3) Soft drink producers which ignore these trends will soon face lower profits. (4) Some consumers are baffled by the wide range of choices in retail outlets. (5) Research indicates that these new markets are likely to grow well into the next decade.

_____

18.6 Transitions

■ *Underline once the main transitional devices (transitional words, repeated words, pronouns, and demonstrative adjectives) that enable the reader to see connections between clauses and sentences. Underline twice those that enable the reader to see the connections between paragraphs.*

When students complete a first draft, they consider the job of writing done—and their teachers too often agree. When professional writers complete a first draft, they usually feel that they are at the start of the writing process. When a draft is completed, the job of writing can begin.

That difference in attitude is the difference between amateur and professional, inexperience and experience, journeyman and craftsman. Peter F. Drucker, the prolific business writer, calls his first draft "the zero draft"—after that he can start counting. Most writers share the feeling that the first draft, and all of those which follow, are opportunities to discover what they have to say and how best they can say it.

To produce a progression of drafts, each of which says more and says it more clearly, the writer has to develop a special kind of reading skill. In school we are taught to decode what appears on the page as finished writing. Writers, however, face a different category of possibility and responsibility when they read their own drafts. To them the words on the page are never finished. Each can be changed and rearranged, can set off a chain reaction of confusion or clarified meaning. This is a different kind of reading which is possibly more difficult and certainly more exciting.

—Donald M. Murray,
"The Maker's Eye: Revising Your Own Manuscripts"

Cross-References to the *Practical English Handbook,* Seventh Edition